BLUEPRINTS
The Phonics Book

Helen Hadley

Stanley Thornes (Publishers) Ltd

First published in 1994 by:
Stanley Thornes (Publishers) Ltd
Ellenborough House
Wellington Street
CHELTENHAM GL50 1YD
England

Reprinted 1995 (twice)

A catalogue record for this book is available from the British Library.

ISBN 0–7487–1729–3

Typeset by Tech-Set, Gateshead, Tyne & Wear
Printed and bound in Great Britain

CONTENTS

PREFACE

WHAT IS *THE PHONICS BOOK?*

Blueprints: The Phonics Book is a set of materials to be used alongside a school's reading programme. It is independent of any series of reading books or specific reading material and provides a range of learning tasks which encourage the growth of phonic skills. The aim is to develop these skills so that children can read and write confidently. This book is based on practical experience, sound educational practice and follows the requirements of the National Curriculum for English in Reading, Writing and Spelling. The activities provide varied and extensive opportunities to develop children's knowledge and use of phonics cues. The cues are introduced in a systematic way and cover the phonemes and consonant blends children are likely to meet during their primary years.

Blueprints: The Phonics Book is suited to either a whole school approach or as supporting material to more eclectic styles. The material can be used with Nursery children and with older pupils who have little or no knowledge of the use of phonics in learning to read and write. In *The Phonics Book* each step along the learning path leads naturally to the next one, giving it structure and continuity. Particular pages or sections, however, can be used separately according to need, thus giving flexibility.

The book is divided into two parts. Part One discusses what phonics is and its role in learning to read, write and spell. Part Two has 113 copymasters with background notes and suggestions for the use of work sheets, word lists, games and activities. Some generic copymasters are included for teachers to adapt to their own specific requirements. The forty or more sounds of English are introduced in a systematic way along with the letter strings and activities to show how to blend them to make words. The copymasters involve the children in using their eyes, ears, mouth and memory to learn letter sounds and blends.

Some years ago I was appointed to a school where the low level of reading and writing gave cause for concern. Only 16 per cent of children were reading a year or more above their chronological age, and 56 per cent were, in fact, a year or more below. We, the staff, discussed changes to the current practice in the school. Placing our existing reading books into ten bands, we supplemented them at each level with a number of little books, both fact and fiction, as quickly as finances allowed. We also devised and introduced a structured programme for teaching phonics.

Within two years the level of reading competence had changed dramatically, reversing the previous figures. Only 14 per cent of children were now reading a year or more below their chronological age and 59 per cent were reading a year or more above at the age of seven. All this in a school where the average IQ was well below the mean! Most importantly the children were reading with confidence and enjoyment and were not afraid to attempt to read new words using their newly-acquired phonic skills. They wanted to write and because of their willingness to try to write unfamiliar words the content of their written work was much more interesting and improved in both quality and quantity.

Experience and research by people like Dr Joyce Morris widened our understanding so the programme grew and developed over the years, but, in essence it remained the same.

The new Proposals for English in the National Curriculum highlight the need for phonics to be taught as one of the word attack skills that children need to have at their fingertips. *The Phonics Book* is based on the phonics programme we developed over the years but with minor changes to ensure that it is in line with the demands of the new proposals and with current thinking on the teaching of phonics.

Helen Hadley
June 1994

PART 1
UNDERSTANDING
PHONICS

INTRODUCTION

The ability to read is the basis of all learning. It is through reading that new worlds of learning, thought, and experience are opened to us. We want children to learn to read and write as quickly as possible, but both are complex tasks requiring word attack skills, thinking ability, and prior knowledge. Phonics is the word attack skill we are concerned with in *Blueprints: The Phonics Book,* that is teaching children to analyse the sound value of letters and syllables and to synthesise them.

Phonics is one of the most valuable word attack skills that children acquire. It enables them to tackle written words that they do not recognise, gain from clues in the context, or from language expectation. Basically it is a synthetic approach which pays attention to the sound that letters and letter clusters represent. These sounds are taught in a systematic way by beginning with single letter sounds and then blending the letters into words. There are only a certain number of words children can learn by sight so phonics gives them the confidence to approach unfamiliar words. The earlier children develop this confidence, the faster the progress they make in both reading and writing.

The English language is not a rule-driven truly phonetic language, it is complex and, to some extent, irregular. It has almost 3,000 sound combinations and 104 different ways of representing vowels. The sounds in the English language are represented by single letters or letter-strings which make up the forty plus phonemes of the language.

A phoneme is the smallest unit of speech which distinguishes one word from another. For example, it is the 'b' at the beginning of 'bet' which distinguishes 'bet' from 'get', 'jet', 'met' and 'set'. A variety of letters can also represent a single phoneme: c, k, ck – cat, kite, back; al, au, aw, or and ou – walk, August, awful, for, fought. One phoneme can also represent different sounds, for example 'a' has at least seven. Yet 80 per cent of words in general use are regular, which is reason enough to justify teaching phonics.

However, there are limitations we should be aware of when teaching children phonics.

- Phonics is an aid, a word attack skill, to be learnt and used when appropriate, not a total scheme in itself.
- The spelling of over 80 per cent of words is very close to recognisable patterns, but most of the remaining 20 per cent do not have a direct sound/symbol relationship and have to be learnt by sight.
- Splitting words into their sound components, if not uttered correctly, can prevent the development of reading fluency.
- The mechanical nature of phonics ignores comprehension and response to the words read.
- Reading for meaning must go on alongside phonics if children are to extend their thoughts, their feelings, and deepen their understanding of themselves, and others, through reading and writing.
- Children can become so intrigued and pleased with their ability to 'build' words on a letter/sound basis that they focus too closely on building words in the text, and lose the flow and with it, the enjoyment of reading.

Each of these points is valid but, if we are aware of them and compensate for them, the knowledge of learning letter sounds and blends is of great benefit to the majority of children, and speeds the process of learning to read and write.

THE NATIONAL CURRICULUM

The English, Scottish and Northern Ireland Guidelines are all concerned with the range of word attack skills which children need to unlock unfamiliar words. *English in the National Curriculum* comes down very firmly on the side *for* teaching phonics. It stresses the importance of phonics teaching and defines the skills children need to acquire.

Even when the teaching of phonics was out of fashion many of us continued to help children to learn letter sounds, blends and digraphs and to use them in their reading, writing and spelling. We knew that it was one of the essential skills children needed to acquire and it is good to see that the National Curriculum now supports this view so strongly. The programmes of study for Key Stages 1 and 2 are summarised below.

KEY STAGE 1: READING

■ **2. Key Skills**

a Pupils should be taught to read with fluency, accuracy and understanding and enjoyment, building on what they already know… Pupils should be taught the alphabet, and be made aware of the sounds of spoken language in order to develop phonological awareness. They should also be taught to use various approaches to word identification and recognition…

b Within a balanced and coherent programme, pupils should be taught to use the following knowledge, understanding and skills.

Phonic knowledge, focusing on the relationships between print symbols and sound patterns. Opportunities should be given for:

■ recognising alliteration, sound patterns and rhyme, and relating these to patterns in letters;
■ considering syllables in longer words;
■ identifying initial and final sounds in words;
■ identifying and using a comprehensive range of letters and sounds, including combinations of letters, blends and digraphs, and paying specific attention to their use on the formation of words;
■ recognising inconsistencies in phonic patterns;
■ recognising that some letters do not produce a sound themselves but influence the sound of others.

KEY STAGE 1: WRITING

■ **2. Key Skills**

d In **spelling**, pupils should be taught to:

■ use their knowledge of sound–symbol relationships and phonological patterns;
■ recognise and use simple spelling patterns;
■ write common letter strings within familiar and common words;

■ spell commonly occurring words.

Pupils should be taught to check the accuracy of their spelling… identifying initial letters as a means of locating words… Close attention should be paid to word families.

KEY STAGE 2: READING

■ **2. Key Skills**

a …pupils should be taught to extend their phonic and graphic knowledge to include more complex patterns and irregularities.

KEY STAGE 2: WRITING ▶

■ **2. Key Skills**

d In **spelling** they should be taught:

■ the relevance of word families...
■ alternative ways of writing the same sound.

Pupils should be taught to:

■ memorise the visual patterns of words...
■ use appropriate terminology, including vowel and consonant.

ATTAINMENT TARGET 2: READING ▶

Level 1
Pupils recognise familiar words in simple texts. They use their knowledge of letters and sound–symbol relationships in order to read words and to establish meaning...

Level 2
They use more than one strategy, such as phonic, graphic, syntactic and contextural, in reading unfamiliar words and establishing meaning.

ATTAINMENT TARGET 3: WRITING ▶

Level 2
...Simple monosyllabic words are usually spelt correctly, and where there are inaccuracies the alternative is phonetically plausible.

SCOTTISH NATIONAL GUIDELINES ▶

The *Scottish National Guidelines on English Language 5–14* Programme of Study for **Reading** states that pupils should:

● learn the basic skills of reading through a systematic and progressive programme, which should incorporate an initial sight vocabulary and also develop phonic and blending skills, and skills of word attack.

Spelling in Writing Programme of Study the Guidelines state that:

● Level A — Pupils should be given an interest in words, how they sound, how they are made and the patterns within them: Pupils should become alert to the structure of words and know that words are built from constituent parts.

NORTHERN IRELAND STATUTORY ORDERS ▶

The *Northern Ireland English Statutory Orders* follow similar lines.
The Programme of Study for **Reading** — Pupils should:

Level 2
● notice how words are constructed and spelled, and they should use a range of strategies to identify unfamiliar words in texts and use picture, context and phonic cues in reading a book new to them.

Level 3
● use, sometimes independently, a range of strategies

when identifying unfamiliar words in texts, for example, use context and other cues when making sense of new material.

Activities for all these National Curriculum requirements for phonic teaching are in the section 'Introducing Phonics' and in Part 2 of *Blueprints: The Phonics Book*. Through these activities children are provided with a good working knowledge to enable them to use phonics in their reading, writing and spelling and teachers are given some help and ideas to encourage them to teach early phonics effectively.

PHONIC SOUNDS AND BLENDS

SOUNDS

A number of lists have been produced to suggest ways of teaching letter sounds and phonemes. There are slight variations between these published lists but, basically, they agree that twenty-one single consonant sounds are constant with only five digraphs, 'sh', 'ch', 'th' (voiced), 'th' (unvoiced) and 'ng' added to this list. Some lists of basic sounds and phonemes state that the letters 'k', 'q' and 'x' duplicate 'c' and 's' and so leave them out. I feel that it is important for children to learn the sound of every letter in the alphabet, and then look for any similarities.

The published lists of the five vowels suggest many different combinations, and it is this plethora of combinations that causes most of the problems in learning to read and write English. Working with vowels is rather like opening a can of worms, vowels wriggle in and out of each other, forming and reforming the sounds of letter clusters to give twenty basic vowel sounds. In their short form vowels are constant, but put them with another vowel or consonant, such as 'r' or 'w' or 'll', and the sounds proliferate. There *is* consistency, however, and once children know the options for the letter strings they need to read and write, they can proceed with confidence.

At our school we gave considerable thought to the best way to present these many letter sounds. We decided to introduce each one separately, and to confirm one letter string for a particular sound, or phoneme, before introducing another. The letters were grouped according to where they are felt in the mouth: the tip of the tongue, the lips, the back of the tongue, and the front of the mouth. This grouping sharpens the child's ability to hear and differentiate between letter sounds.

BLENDS

A blend is when two or more letters are put together and, if you listen carefully, you can hear each sound distinctly. Children need to hear and see what blending is and how it works.

Begin by blending c v c (consonant vowel consonant) words (can) then c c v c (frog) and c v c c (pest). The next step is to group common initial blends: consonants 'l' or 'r', 's' with one or more consonants e.g. 'cl', 'fl', 'spl'; doubled consonants e.g. 'll', 'ff', 'ss'; 't' plus another consonant e.g. 'st', 'ft'; final blends e.g. '-mp', '-ng'; and consonant digraphs e.g. 'th', 'sh'. Once these are confirmed move on to long vowel sounds: common double vowels, marker or magic 'e', diphthongs, and vowels with 'r'.

The final group, includes the schwa sound, 'wh', soft 'c' and 'g', and silent letters. These letters are not actual sounds, but children need to know how to react to these letter strings when they meet them. There is not room to study them in a book of this length but they have been listed below for information. You can design activities for these other phonic sounds (numbers 15–20 in the list following) on the lines of those in Section 9 using the master sheets provided and using the sound flash cards in Section 7.

Letter sounds should not be taught in isolation, they must have word associations. Whenever you introduce a letter say a whole word first, then the sound of the initial letter e.g. ant, 'a'. By saying the word first, children are helped to hear the true phonic sound of the letter which they can replicate when saying the letter's sound.

When blending sounds to make a word be very careful how the sounds are pronounced. If the sounds are separated and given emphasis as here in CUH-UH-TER, when they are joined together the word formed is CUTTER. Keep the sounds short and clear so that only a short clear sound is given. First write the whole word or use a 'flash card' and pass your finger under the letters saying the sound to make the whole word as your finger travels under it: 'CUUT'.

Apart from the need to know initial sounds and to be able to blend them into words, children need to know how letters are affected by others in close proximity, and the options to select from, when a constituent sound can be represented by more than one letter cluster. This is what *The Phonics Book* sets out to do.

The list on the page facing shows the order in which commonly used phonics should be introduced and identifies the groups to which they belong. All but a few of the sounds listed are covered in *The Phonics Book*.

SINGLE LETTER SOUNDS

1. Short vowel sounds   a   e   i   o   u

2. Tip of the tongue sounds   d   l   n   s   t   and   r

3. Lip sounds   b   f   m   p   v   w

4. Back of the tongue sounds   c   g   h   k   y

5. Front of mouth sounds   j   q   x   z

CONSONANT BLENDS AND DIGRAPHS

6. Consonant digraphs (i)   sh   ch   th (voiced)   th (unvoiced)

7. Initial blends
bl   cl   fl   gl   pl   sl   spl
br   cr   dr   fr   gr   pr   tr
sc   sk   sm   sp   sn   st   scr   spr   str
dw   sw   tw

8. Final blends
-sk   -sp   -st
-ct   -ft   -lt   -nt   -pt   -xt   -lk   -lm   -lp
-mp   -nd   -nk
-ddle   -pple   -ttle   -ndle   -ngle   -nkle

9. Doubled consonants   -dd   -ff   -gg   -ll   -ss   -tt   -zz   and   ck

10. Consonant digraphs (ii)   wh   -ng   ph   -tch   -dge

DOUBLE VOWELS AND DIPTHONGS

11. Double vowel   ea   ee   oa   oo (book)   oo (spoon)

12. Marker e   a-e   i-e   o-e   u-e   e-e

13. Diphthong   ai   ay   oe   oi   oy   ou
ow (cow)   ow (snow)   aw   ew
ie   igh   ight

14. Vowels with r (i)   ar   er   ir   or   ur   ear   eer   oar   are   air

5

OTHER PHONIC SOUNDS NOT COVERED IN THIS BOOK

15. Long sound   a (angel)   e (me)   i (island)   o (go)   u (music)   y (my)

16. Vowels with 'r' (ii)   ure   ire   ore   ere   oor

17. Other endings   ed ild ind all ould ound   y (sunny)   ough-various

18. Schwa sound   'uh' (alone, lemon, writer, giant)

19. Soft c & g   before e & i

20. Silent letters   g-gnaw   k-knee   b-lamb

TEACHING PHONICS

AUDITORY DISCRIMINATION ▶

Children need to develop both auditory and visual discrimination to become fluent readers and writers of English because, although so many words can be built phonetically, 20 per cent still have to be learnt by the look of the word. Children also need these skills to help develop the automatic responses that fluent reading requires. Some dyslexic children who have a poor visual memory, but some auditory acuity, can be helped by structured phonic teaching.

From the day children enter school they should begin to develop the aural and visual skills needed for reading and writing. Children's auditory acuity is developing throughout their Infant School years but is not fully developed until later in their school life. Some children's auditory acuity is never going to be sharp and, just a few of those with poor auditory acuity or more severe problems, may find phonics is no help at all. In *The Phonics Book* the plan for teaching the sounds of individual letters is structured to assist the development of auditory acuity.

Games for aural skills
When playing the following games the children who answer first are those with good auditory acuity, the later callers are usually mimicking earlier responses but it helps them to make the association and is preliminary to developing their own aural skills.

● Point to two or three items in the room which begin with the same sound and say their names. Ask children to give you a word beginning with the same sound.
● Ask them to tell you the sound they hear at the beginning of two or three given words (e.g. pet, pin, pig) and to give you a word beginning with the same sound.
● Slowly say the sounds of a short familiar word and ask them if they can hear a word. Children can either call out the word they hear or put up their hands – it depends on the way you wish your class to respond. Repeat the word slowly two or three times. Try a few more three or four lettered words, preferably those connected with a story or rhyme you have just told them, or with a picture, book, or item on display which you have talked about.

● Show the children a number of items then place them behind a solid screen, say the beginning sound of one and ask the children to tell you what it is. Hold up the item when it has been guessed. After a while, play the game without showing the children the items you are putting behind the screen. They then have to search their minds for likely words beginning with that sound. If the word they suggest begins with the same sound, but is not the item, say 'Yes, your word does begin with the same sound but it is not what I have in my hand'. This way children are confirmed in the correctness of their response to the phonic sound.

● Say the sounds of a word which is displayed around the classroom. Once the children have guessed the word, ask one of them to run a finger under the word and repeat it. Later that day and on succeeding days revise words learnt this way, so building up this growing bank of words with them.

● Once the children have learnt the sounds in Group 1, and at least one vowel, write a cvc word on the board, or make one with the cards from Section 7. Ask the children to say the sounds in the word as you run your finger underneath it and to tell you what the word says. Not only does this help children to blend sounds into words, but confirms what reading is and makes the links between reading and writing.

Play these kinds of games every day. Before the children start working on a sound sheet focus your games on that particular sound or letter string.

READING ▶

Phonics helps readers to tackle unknown or unfamiliar words with confidence. If we are able to hear the constituent sounds within a word and blend them with a reasonable degree of accuracy, we read, write and spell at a faster pace. Research has shown that phonics methods help children to make progress in reading, if introduced systematically alongside children's normal reading.

Playing phonic games orally should start with Nursery children but no attempt should be made to foster phonics in written form until children have begun to learn to read. It is only in this context that children will recognise the purpose and usefulness of phonics.

Once children have established a store of 'look and say' words they begin to recognise that each word has its own pattern. This is the time to start phonics. Phonics teaches them that most words can be broken down into a series of sounds which, when placed in a particular sequence, form a specific word and that placing the sounds in another sequence forms a different word.

Draw attention to the initial sounds of words in their early reading books, and around the classroom, then work with unknown words or words they do know but which are unfamiliar when written down. Work from single letter/sound responses to blending sounds into letter strings or words, and blending those strings or words into other words, as soon as children know sufficient sounds to do so.

Learning to read solely through phonics would be a bit like learning to play an instrument by practising only five-finger exercises and scales. Learning an instrument begins with playing simple tunes and then adding skills and techniques. This way, the children have the joy of playing recognisable melodies while developing the skills essential to becoming better instrumentalists. In reading we want children to have the pleasure and fun of reading stories by 'look and say' methods, but we also need to build in phonic skills so they become both fluent and independent readers.

If phonics is used to identify an unfamiliar word, without having made sense of the context it is in, children are less likely to become successful readers and writers. Knowing the text and using both visual and non-visual information allows them to consider which words might be suitable, then use their phonic skills to determine what the word says.

Some children learn to synthesise sounds rapidly and soon transfer that to their reading, others take a much longer time. Consequently, while some children will sail through the *The Phonics Book* programme with little need for revision or reinforcement, others will need all the support, work and games that you and this book can provide.

WRITING ▶

The main advantages of phonics acquisition is that by knowing letter/sound combinations children are encouraged to have a go at words they need for writing.

Children first learn to use phonics to help with unfamiliar words, but later on they bring their growing knowledge of the visual patterning to write then check to see if the word they have written looks right – just as we adults do.

Adults have an automatic response to thousands of words developed through meeting them many times in their reading, and practising them in their writing. Words are memorised without being aware of it.

Children will develop this automatic response over time with exposure to a range of reading books, language support material, and help. Able children need to see a word twenty times before it becomes their own and they can use it at will, less able children need to see a word a hundred or more times before being able to write it without assistance.

The Phonics Book concentrates on using phonics to develop an automaticity to as many words and letter strings as possible, so giving children the confidence to tackle most of the words they need.

SPELLING ▶

We want children to write what they want to say, then go back and check the spelling, but many young children like to get their work correct at the first attempt. They hesitate over words they are unsure of, which holds back the freedom of expression we are trying to engender in their writing. A knowledge of phonics gives children the confidence to write down a near representation of what they are trying to say, which frees them to write.

When copying or correcting a word, children should always write the word as a whole, not letter by letter, so they practise the whole word and feel its correct motor pattern flowing from their hand onto the paper.

Look, Visualise and Write
Phonics helps to develop the visual cueing needed in the Look, Visualise and Write technique of learning to spell, a technique which is encouraged throughout *The Phonics Book*. This method encourages children to look closely at a word, study its ascenders, descenders, and minims, and to look for parts of it they may recognise. They 'photograph' the word in their mind, and see it behind their eye-lids, then write the word from memory. When checking a word ask children to tick the letters that are in the correct place. They soon see which part, if any, they have to focus on to write it correctly next time.

WHEN AND HOW ▶

It is not a question of *whether* to use phonics but *when* and *how*. Most children are ready for phonics once they have read a few simple books with one or two lines of text on a page.

The chart below suggests the level of phonics one

would expect to be teaching in a particular year. Obviously all children move at their own pace, some more quickly than others, and this should be encouraged.

	Level of reading	Phonic work
Year 1	beginning	whole word recognition
		initial sounds
		short vowels
	developing skills	final sounds
		3 letter word building c+v+c (p+a+t)
		cv+c (pa+t) and c+vc (p+at)
Year 2	moving forward	initial and final consonant blends
		build longer regular words ccvc
Year 3	mastery	long vowel sounds
Lower juniors	fluency	other sound changes

If children only use the look/say method as a way of unlocking new words they will make limited progress in their junior schools.

The Phonics Book is flexible and can be dipped into at Junior level to fill gaps in previous learning.

BEGINNING PHONICS ▶

Most children need a number of activities to prepare them for phonic work.

Labels
Put labels on everything. Start with single nouns and then add adjectives. Before you put it up say the word slowly, running your finger from left to right, then say the initial sound. Ask the children to look at other labels and to see if another one begins with the same letter.

Give a group of children the labels and some 'Blu-tack'®. Ask them to fix the labels on the correct objects. If someone else has labelled an object already they must find another example. The group then checks that the labelling is correct. If one is wrongly placed they must say why.

Names
Give each child a card with both first and family names written in the school's handwriting style. It is important for them to learn both names. Ask the child to read his/her name from the card and run an index finger under the word as it is said.

Children should write their first name at the beginning of any piece of writing. Encourage them to write as much of it as possible from memory. Once the first name can be written from memory, the second name should be added. At first my class used to write their first names then add the initial letter of their surname. The remaining letters were added gradually. On the back of their drawings and paintings children wrote their initials for identification, so drawing attention to the initial letters and gaining an awareness of the meaning and association of its sound.

Sound Corner
Make a display corner for a letter or letter string. If possible cover a table with a cloth or paper whose colour and/or texture can be associated with the letter's sound e.g. blue, black or brown for 'b', 'bl' or 'br', shiny fabric for 'sh', corrugated cardboard for 'c'. Drape fabric or put up a sheet of activity paper for a backcloth and put a large cut-out letter on it. Add appropriate pictures and label them clearly.

Cut letters from felt, fabrics of different kinds, and

sandpaper as well as using letters from educational suppliers to put on the table. Mark the start point of the letter with a green dot or sticker and a red one to show where to stop as per the letters in Section 1. Encourage children to trace the letters with the index finger of their writing hand. Let them practise the letter both large and small using a whole range of media – paint, crayon, felt pen, chalk and pastels.

Display items beginning with the same letter and label them clearly, e.g. *can, card, cap, crab, cat.* Encourage children to loan pictures and items for a specific letter to go on the letter/sound table. Talk about the things they bring in. Draw appropriate adjectives from them which begin with the same sound, e.g. *a blue ball, a big balloon.* Let them suggest the sounds for the letters in the word as you write the label. Talk about the sounds while you write.

Talk about examples of the 'sound' around the room, their names, their clothes, what they eat, where they live, T.V. programmes, etc. Link the letter sound as much as possible with their real world. Put a sheet of paper and felt pens beside the table, and ask children to look for the letters in their reading books and to write any word they find on the list. At the end of the day go through the words listed and encourage children to read out the sentence they found containing the word.

Ask them to listen for words beginning with the sound and tell a neighbour. At the end of the day ask them to share any they have remembered.

Cover a table with clean display material. Put up a notice 'Find things for our table beginning with 'b'.' Read the notice with the children and give them time to find items around the room to display. Make certain such items are accessible. Have ready a pile of cards for labelling.

Use the sound as much as possible in your spoken language and ask children to signal when they hear the sound. The signal should be unobtrusive, perhaps a touch of the nose for 'n' or the chin for 'ch'. Respond with a smile or a nod. At the end of the session ask for feedback on the words they heard beginning with the sound. Once children have participated in a range of similar activities they are ready for *The Phonics Book.*

Listening for sounds
The following activities can be adapted to any stage of phonics learning, used as refreshers or for filling odd moments during the day.

● Say three words beginning with the same sound e.g. 'cut, cat, castle'. Ask the children which sound they hear at the beginning and ask for another word beginning with the same sound.

● Play 'I spy with my little eye something that begins with the same sound as "bat"'. Choose a word beginning with the letter sound they are learning.

● Say the names of two children in the class whose names begin with the same sound, emphasising the initial letter. Ask the children if they notice anything about the names. Ask them to give you two names of people or things that begin with the same sound.

Once the children have command of a few letters add these games:

Sound sentences
Make up sentences and ask the children to tell you the sound you said at the beginning of more than one word. Make up some sentences as a class or in groups.

The Admiral's cat
● Hold up an initial letter (use the flash cards in Section 7) and give the children three or four words to choose from. Write them on the back of the card for you to refer to e.g. 'a' – angry, attractive, appealing.
● Hold up a letter, e.g. 'b', and say 'Is the Admiral's cat is an angry cat, a clumsy cat or a bad cat?'
● Go around the group working through the alphabet, e.g.
The Admiral's cat is an angry cat.
The Admiral's cat is a beautiful cat.
Do not go through the whole of the alphabet with young children or beginners because it makes the game too long and they lose interest.

Kim's game
Place items on a tray or table – start with five building up to twenty items. The children study them for a few minutes before you cover the tray with a cloth. Ask 'What did you see that began with "b" or "m"?' as appropriate. Take out the item they have named without exposing any of the other ones. Continue until all items have been identified or it is obvious that no more will be guessed. Uncover the tray and go through any remaining items asking children to name the item and say its initial letter.

Word games, jingles, rhyming words, alliteration, nursery rhymes, listening games, and tongue twisters add to children's knowledge of sounds. Use sounds and words that are familiar to them, otherwise we are asking for too much at once: comprehension, the word's meaning and alliteration. The aim is to give familiarity, ease of use, and above all confidence in working with sounds and using them in both reading and writing.

SOUND BOOKS ▶

Each child will need a book in which they can paste the word lists from their work sheets. Use either the half-size Infant book 133 × 165 mm, or cut a standard-sized book in half. The Infant books suggested have thirty-six pages, which is ideal for this work. The books chosen must have at least thirty pages, so that the word lists for each letter of the alphabet can be stuck in the book, and those for the common digraphs 'sh', 'ch', and 'th'. You will find it helpful to alphabetise the pages, this way you have a check of the work done by a child, and the child's knowledge of finding letters of the alphabet is increased.

These sound books serve as:

1. a record of the pages on which the child has worked
2. a reminder of phonetic structures
3. a personal dictionary
4. a book to take home and work through with parents
5. a record to inform the child, the parents, and yourselves of the level of learning and progress the child is making.

The sound books should go home daily so children can share the work they have done that day with their parents, or revise work done previously. Before introducing sound books have a meeting with parents to explain how they can help with their child, and photocopy the letter provided at the back of this book to send home. Stress that the books must be returned to school each day, and that parental help and interest means that children will learn more quickly. It also encourages the development of interaction and dialogue between the parent and child.

PART 2
THE
COPYMASTERS

NOTES ON SECTIONS 1–10 ▶

All the common and most useful phonic structures are covered in this book. Single sounds come at the beginning and consonant blends then alternative vowel spellings follow in succeeding sections. There is not room for less frequent phonic structures in a book of this length but all single sounds and the majority of consonant and vowel blends and digraphs are covered which should enable children to make a serious attempt at decoding most words they meet at primary level.

Each of the Sections 1, 3 and 5 have a set style of presentation. Children quickly pick up the way of working, time spent on instruction is cut to the minimum, so giving you more time to teach.

Section 1
Covers the sounds of each letter of the alphabet. They are arranged in clusters relating to the position in the mouth where the sound is made. Being able to differentiate between these similar sounds increases the child's auditory acuity. Handwriting, word building and spelling activities also feature.

Section 2
Draws together and reinforces the work of Section 1 with games and activities.

Section 3
Concentrates on consonants, blending them to form initial or final clusters and making them into words using short vowel sounds. The concept of digraphs is introduced using the common letter strings of 'ch', 'sh' and 'th' (voiced and unvoiced).

Section 4
Draws together and reinforces the work of Section 3 with games and activities.

Section 5
Presents double vowel sounds, diphthongs, and digraphs.

Vowels have always been considered a serious problem for children, or foreigners, learning to read and write English. Charles Fries, however, points out in *Linguistics and Reading,* Hart, Rinehart and Winston, 1964, that 'although critics of English spelling practically always point to the variety of sounds represented by the letter combination ... most spellings for the vowel sound fit into a very few patterns'. This section introduces common long vowel sounds and vowel homophones, including double vowels, the 'marker' or 'magic e' which modifies the vowel sound, diphthongs, and vowels combined with 'r'.

Section 6
Draws together and reinforces the work of Section 5 with games and activities.

Section 7
Is composed of flash cards of useful letters and letter strings for sound recognition and blending activities.

Section 8
Contains seventy lists of ten words each featuring a specific letter string from Sections 3 and 5. Children put the lists in their sound books when they work on the corresponding copymasters.

Section 9
Contains a number of games and activities for both practice and revision. Outline masters of some activities are included for teachers to write in particular phonic structures they wish their children to work on.

Section 10
Contains a colour chart for use with some activities, a phonic check list, a supporting word list, and sample letters to parents about their part in using the sound books and the activities with their children.

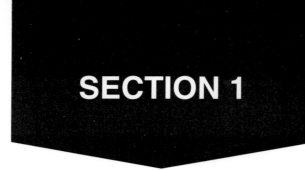

SECTION 1

SINGLE LETTER SOUNDS

C1 –26

This section covers each letter of the alphabet using a multi-sensory approach to learning: list to it, feel it in the mouth, look at it, write it. We want the children to feel the sounds in their mouths and so telling the hand what to write. Next the children should check that it looks right and then check that it is right.

The alphabet is grouped as follows,

Short vowel sounds	a	e	i	o	u	
Tip of the tongue sounds	d	l	n	s	t	and r
Lip sounds	b	f	m	p	v	w
Back of the tongue sounds	c	g	h	k	y	
Front of the mouth sounds	j	q	x	z		

The letters can be taught as follows:

● Write the letter, big and bold, in front of the children saying its sound at the same time. The children stand up and draw a huge letter together, crossing their body line. Talk through how it is formed as the movements are performed, e.g. 'a' – up and round, down and round, straight up, straight down and flick up.

● Ask the children to look for something in the room, or think of a word they know, beginning with the same sound.

● Work through some of the games suggested in Games for aural skills on page 7 and relate them to the letter you are working on before children start working on a copymaster.

Activities

1. Ask the children to trace the large letter shape on the copymaster with the index finger of their writing hand. They should say the letter's sound slowly as they trace it. Each letter starts with an arrow leading from a dot. To trace the letter, follow the direction of the arrows to the cross which marks the end.

2. Using crayons or felt pens, each child should trace the letter inside the letter's broad lines in a continuous movement several times, saying the letter's sound again as it is traced.

3. They should then write over the three guiding letters below, and then write it on their own between the lines.

4. Working in pairs, blend the letters to make the words in the left hand list. Then use the words in sentences spoken aloud to their partners.

5. The words in the right hand list have the sound in the medial or final position. These three and four letter words use the short sound of the vowel. Use the letter cards from Section Seven to help with blending.

6. Search for the letter in the right hand list, circle it and then blend the whole word.

7. After looking at the first word in the left hand list turn the list under, or cover it, and write the word as a whole somewhere on the picture. The word should be written from memory not letter by letter, as copying has no place in teaching phonics. They check the word they have written, letter by letter, against the word in the list and place a line under any letter which is wrong. If the word is wrong, children study the word then cover it or fold the page, and try again to write the whole word from memory. They repeat this method for each word in turn. The right hand list can be worked in a similar way though not necessarily at the same time.

8. Next cut out these word lists and glue them in the appropriate page in the children's sound books. This shows the children the alphabetical place of the letter and its proximity to other letters. It also serves as a record for the teacher of the letters that a child has covered.

9. The sound books can be taken home for the children to work through with their parents. This encourages parents to participate in their children's learning.

10 Colour the pictures.

In some cases the words in the left hand list, including the name, do not start with the letter being learned. This is deliberate as it is preferable to use a simple word with the letter in another position, which children can build, rather than present words where the sound is not true, or the word is too difficult. Similarly, in the right hand list, some words start with the letter being studied. This is because of the way the letter sound changes when in conjunction with other letters and does not keep true to the pure sound, also to keep the words simple.

Associated reading activities

Identify the letter being learnt in magazines and newspapers, then highlight it or circle it with a felt pen. Make up sentences which include the words being built. Look for the letter on classroom notices, around the school and in their reading books.

Handwriting activities

The handwriting element encourages children to get the letter's shape and sound association right from the beginning.

Spelling activities

From the beginning children learn the Look, Visualise and Write technique for learning to spell.

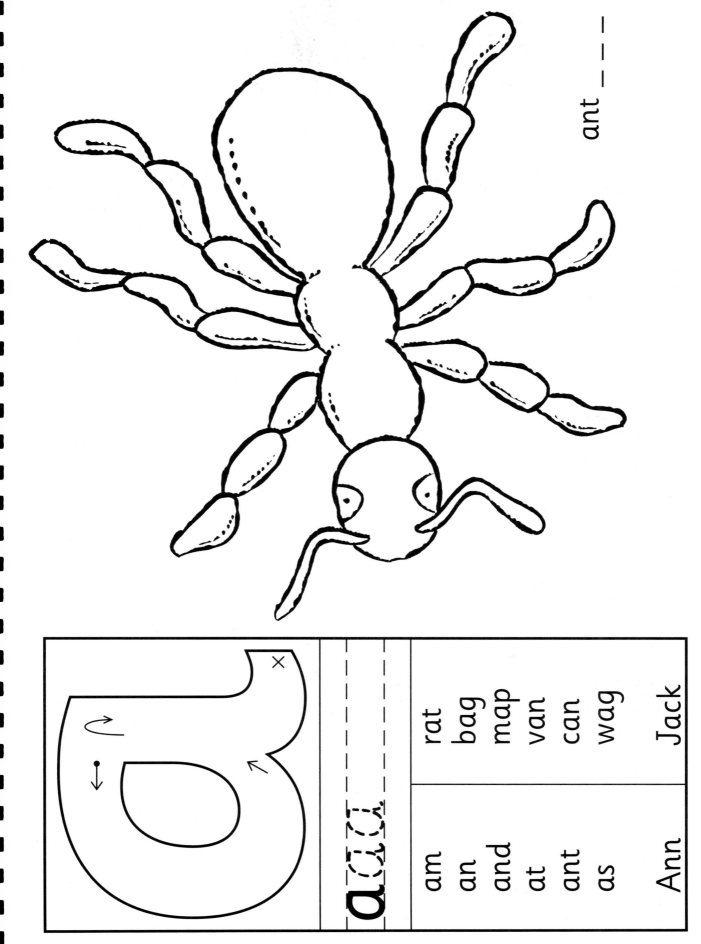

ant _ _ _ _

a a a

am	rat
an	bag
and	map
at	van
ant	can
as	wag
Ann	Jack

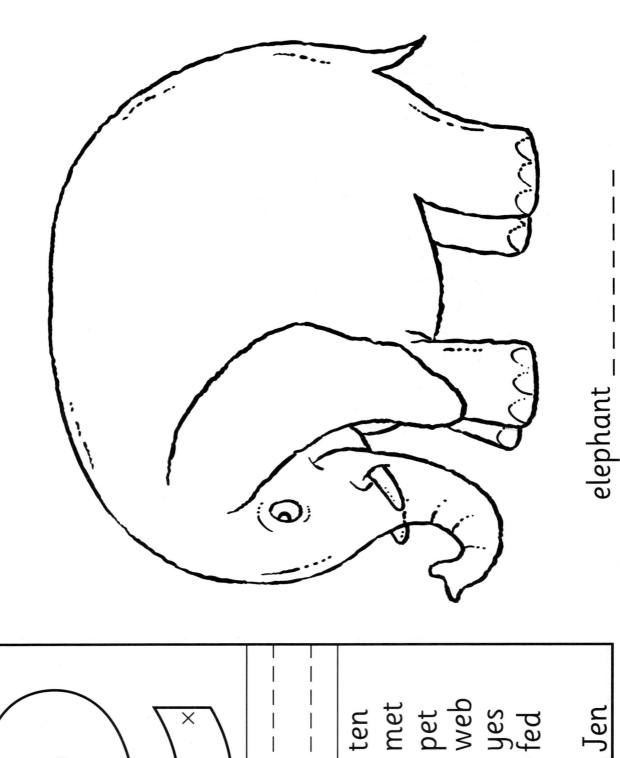

e

egg
end
elf
elk
exit
elm

ten
met
pet
web
yes
fed

Ed

Jen

elephant

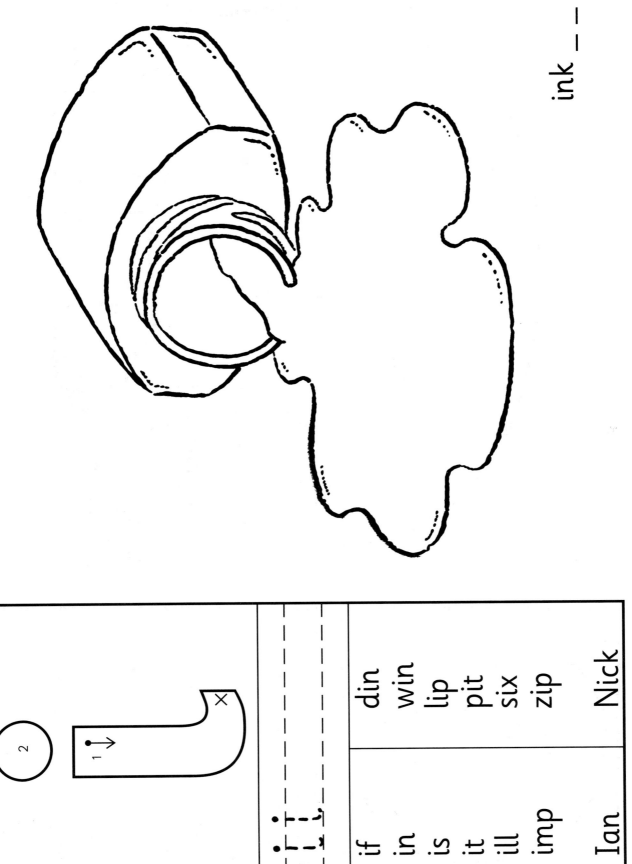

ink _ _ _

2

i i i

if	din
in	win
is	lip
it	pit
ill	six
imp	zip
Ian	Nick

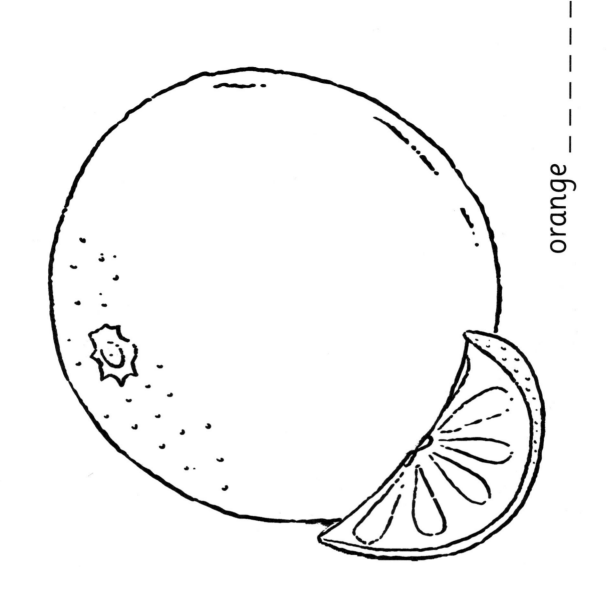

orange – – – –

on	log
odd	bob
off	hop
often	doll
ox	toss
cot	rock
Tom	Bobby

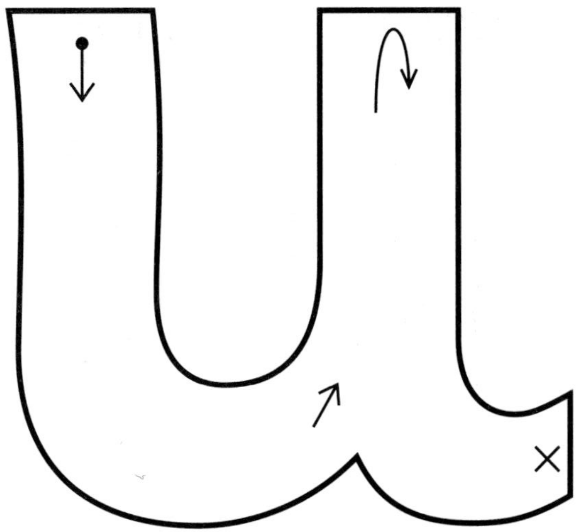

U u

u u u u

Russ	Justin
us	cub
up	fun
upon	mud
upset	pump
bud	fuss
bus	dust

umbrella - - - - -

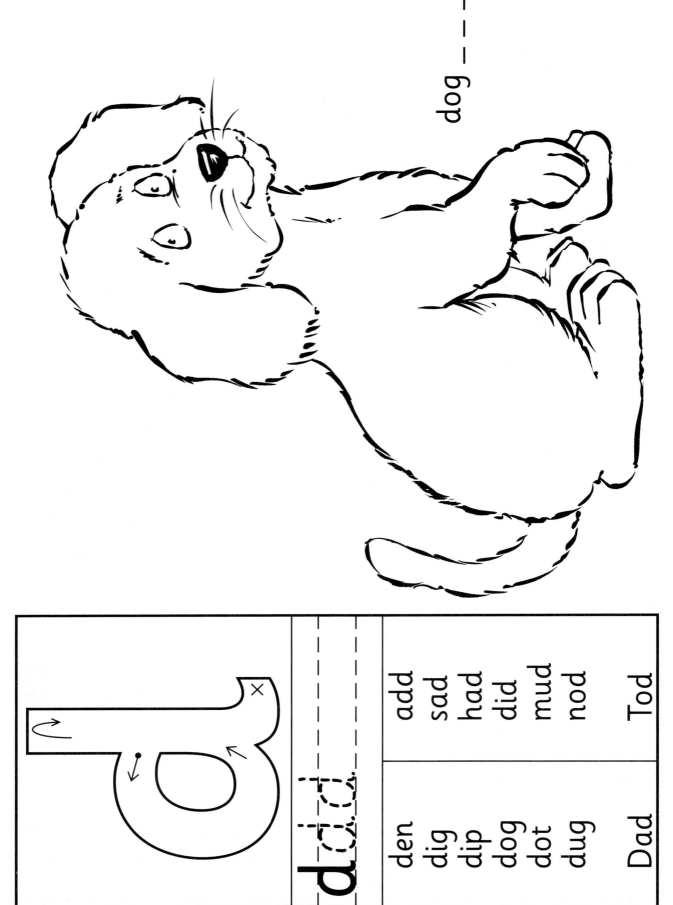

dog — — —

d d d

den	add
dig	sad
dip	had
dog	did
dot	mud
dug	nod
Dad	Tod

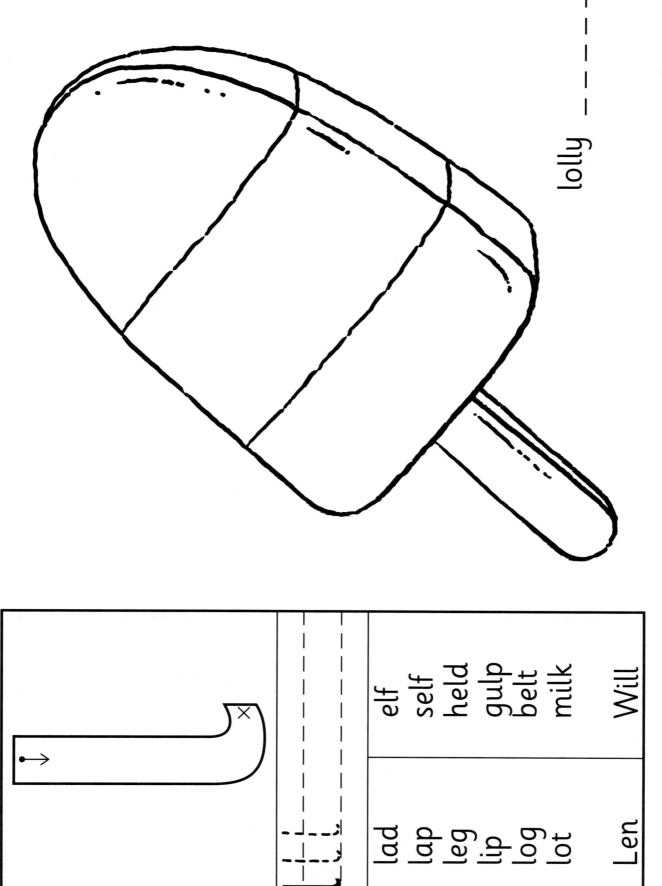

lolly – – – – –

lad	elf
lap	self
leg	held
lip	gulp
log	belt
lot	milk
Len	Will

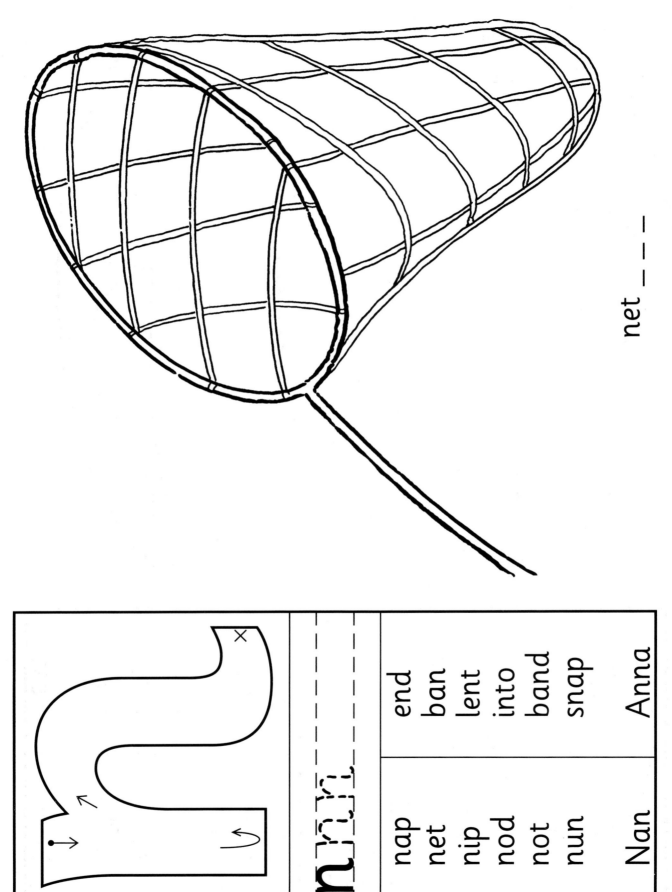

net _ _ _

n n n

nap	end
net	ban
nip	lent
nod	into
not	band
nun	snap
Nan	Anna

S s s

sat   gas
sad   yes
set   us
sit   bus
sun   mess
sums   kiss

Sam   Ross

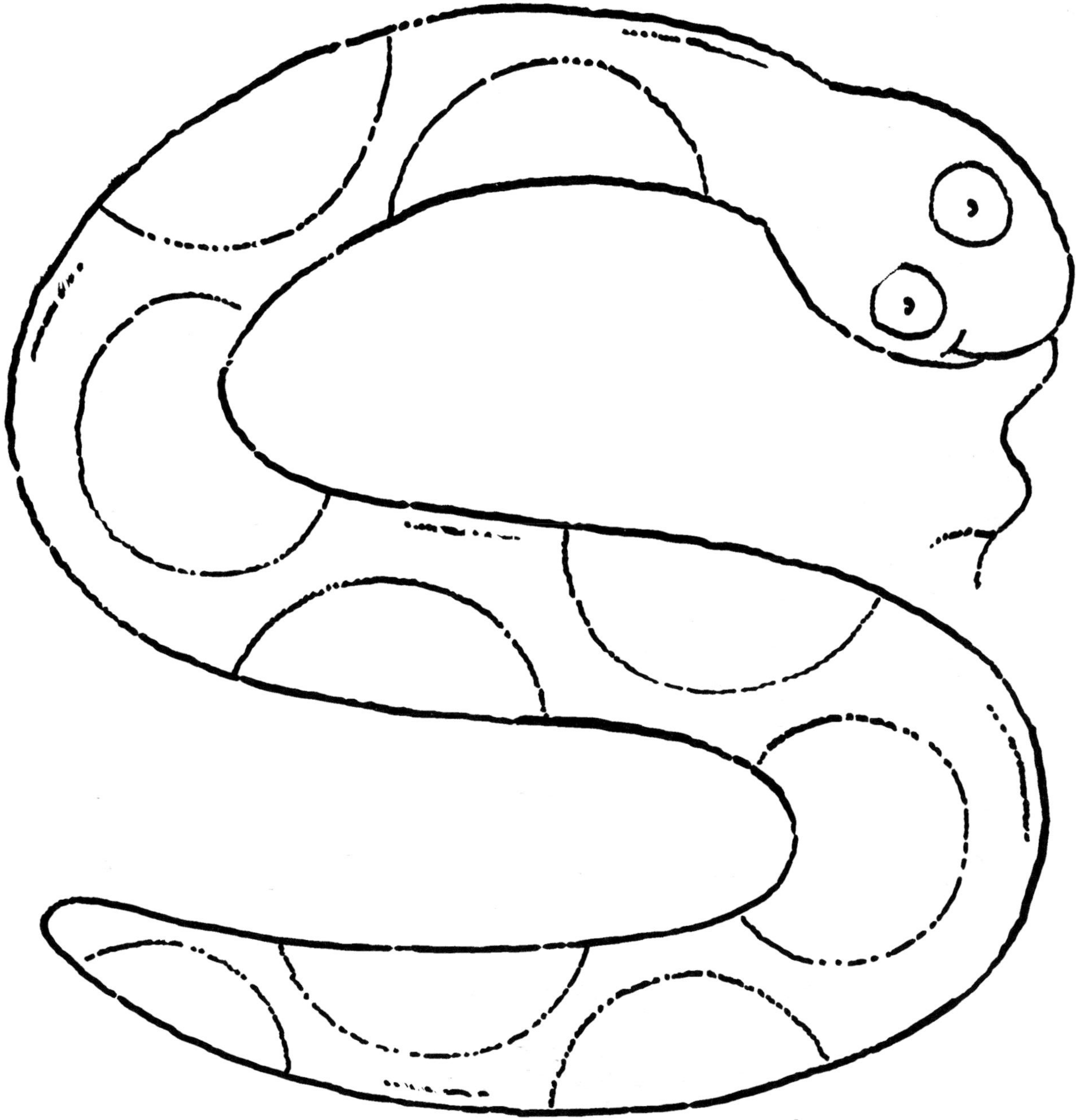

snake _ _ _ _

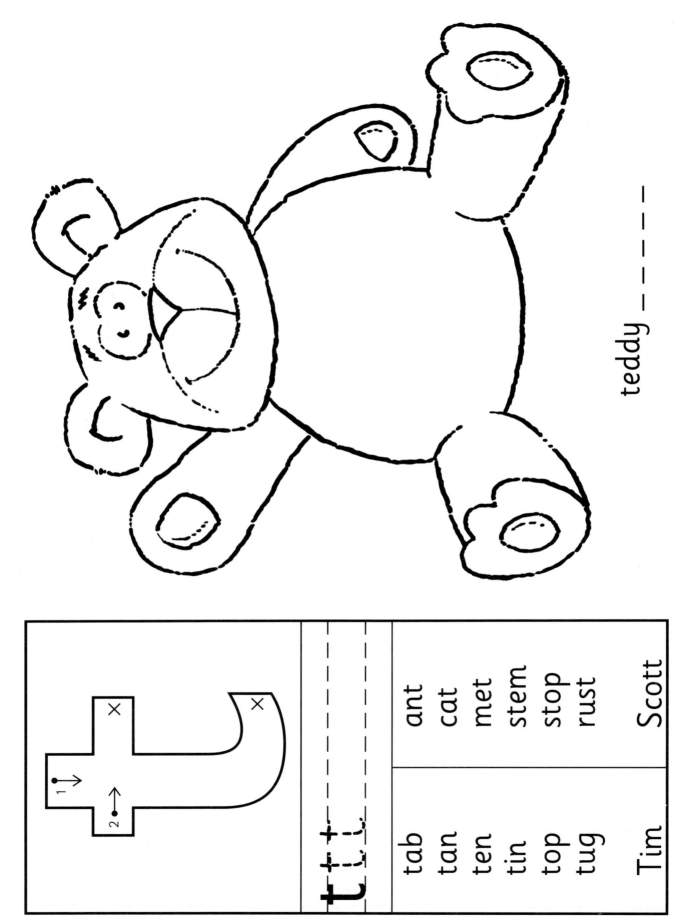

teddy – – – – –

tab   ant
tan   cat
ten   met
tin   stem
top   stop
tug   rust

Tim   Scott

t t t

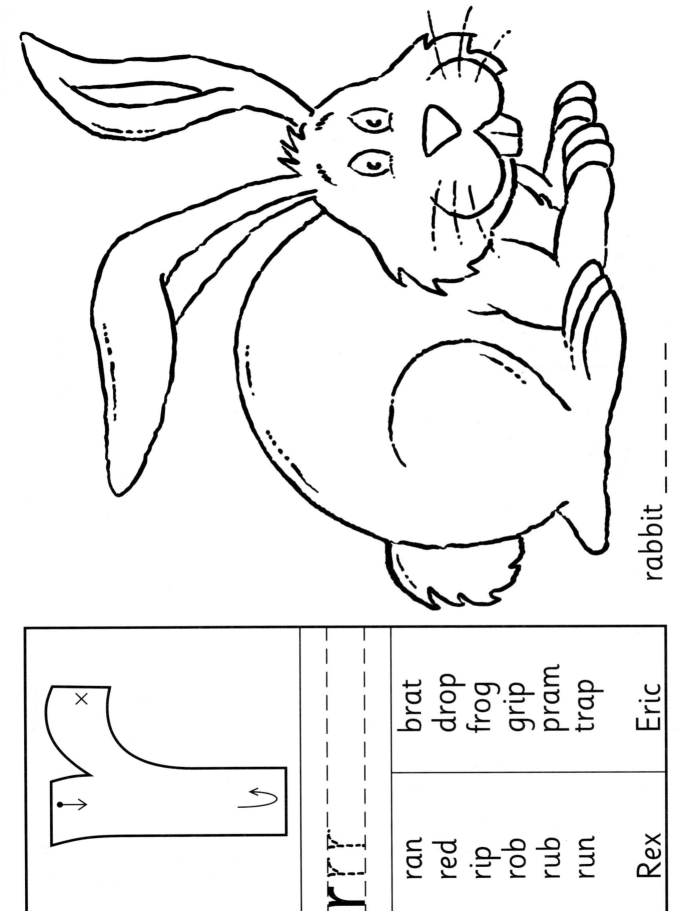

r rr

ran	brat
red	drop
rip	frog
rob	grip
rub	pram
run	trap
Rex	Eric

rabbit _ _ _ _ _ _

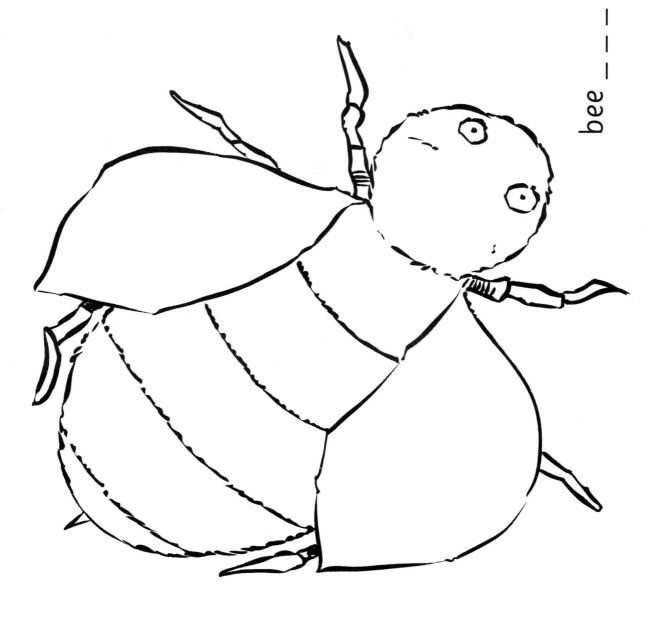

b

bat	cab
bed	rib
big	sob
box	tub
bun	rub
beg	bib
Ben	Rob

bee _ _ _

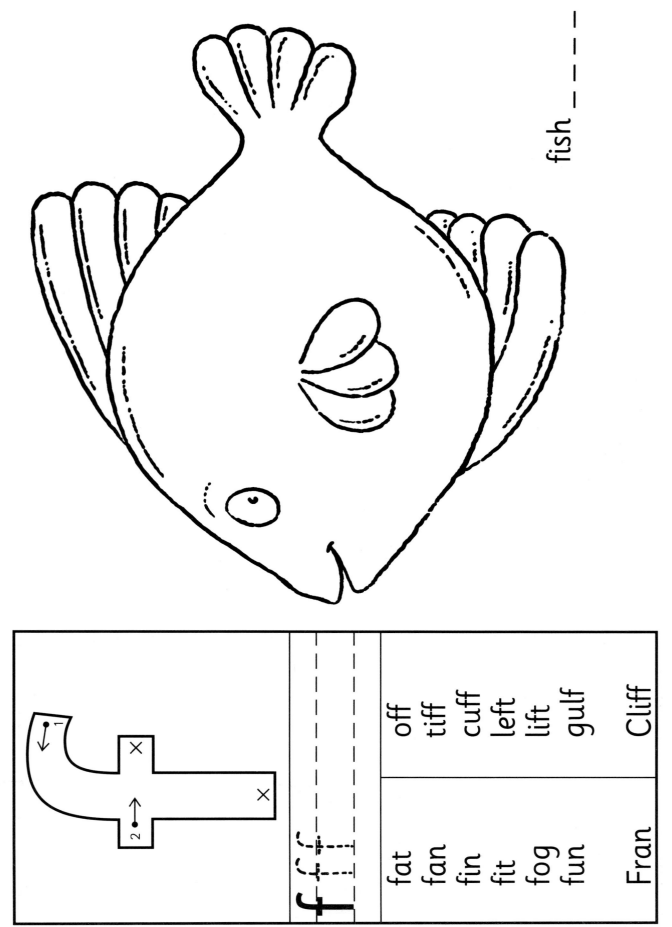

fish _ _ _ _

f f f

fat	off
fan	tiff
fin	cuff
fit	left
fog	lift
fun	gulf
Fran	Cliff

mouse – – – – –

m

m m m

mad	imp
man	ham
men	him
met	sum
mob	film
mud	jump
Mum	Ram

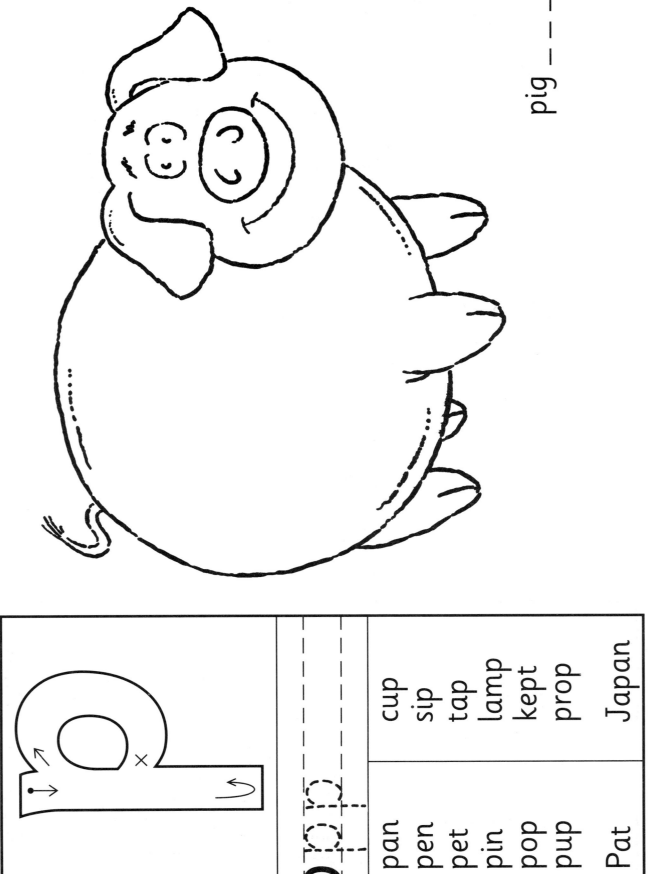

p

p p p

pan	cup
pen	sip
pet	tap
pin	lamp
pop	kept
pup	prop
Pat	Japan

pig – – – –

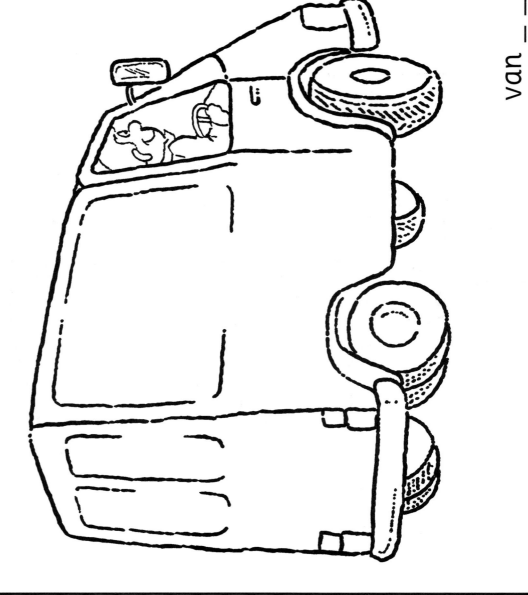

V

v v v

van	seven
vat	velvet
vet	ever
vest	every
vim	given
vex	vivid
Val	Kevin

van _ _ _

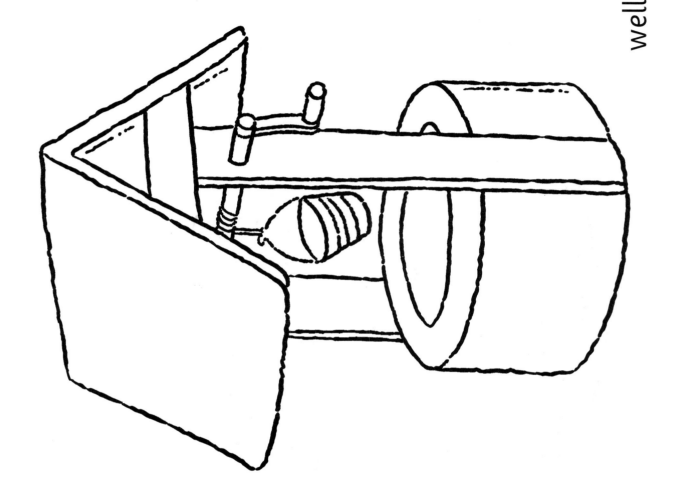

W

w w w

wag	swam
wig	twig
wet	twin
went	swim
west	swag
well	dwell
Wes	Gwen

well _ _ _ _

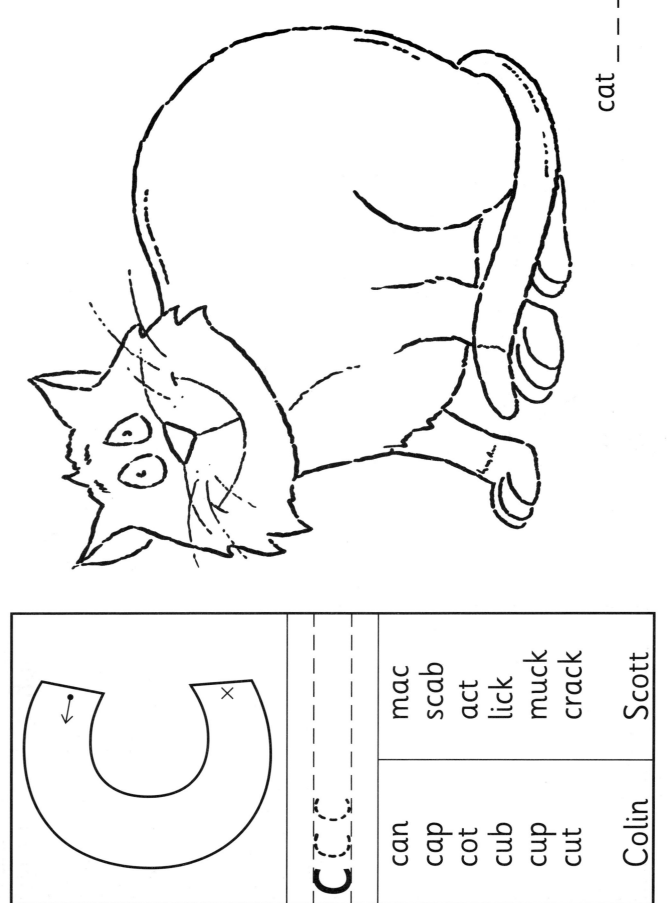

C

c c c

can	mac
cap	scab
cot	act
cub	lick
cup	muck
cut	crack
Colin	Scott

cat _ _ _

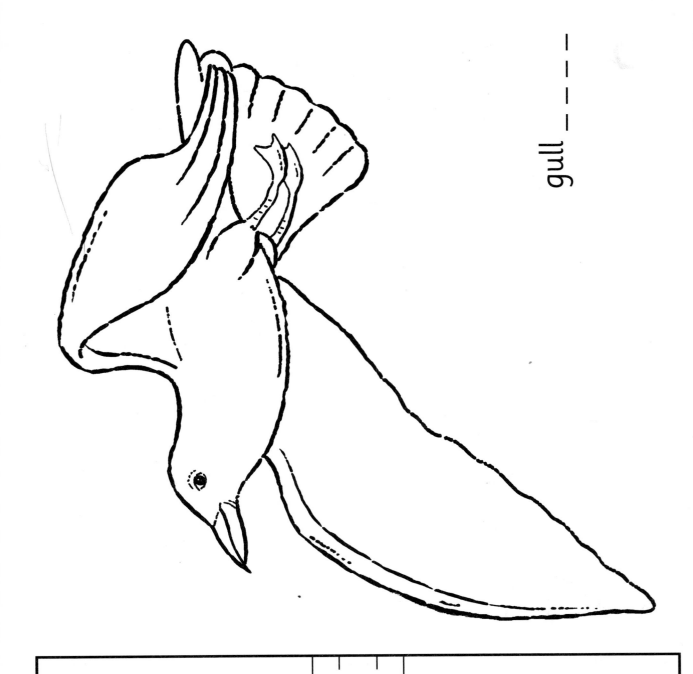

gull – – – – –

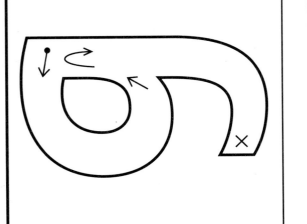

g g

gas	bag
gap	leg
get	cog
gal	hog
gun	jog
gut	wag
Gran	Megan

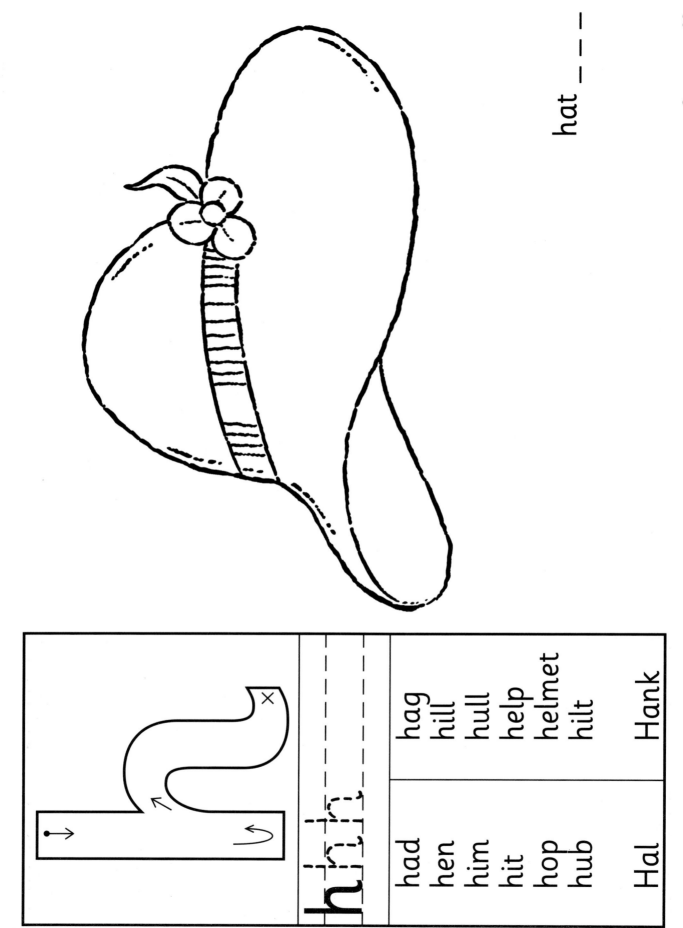

h h h

hat _ _ _

had
hen
him
hit
hop
hub

hag
hill
hull
help
helmet
hilt

Hal

Hank

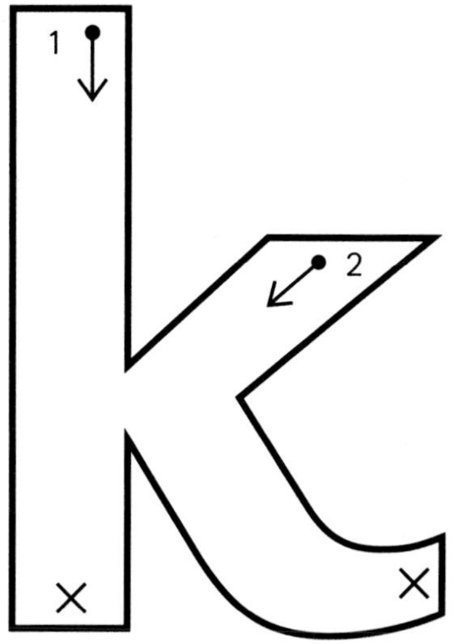

kite _ _ _

K

k k k

kid	elk
kit	ink
kip	skid
kill	skin
kiss	skip
kept	kick
Ken	Mick

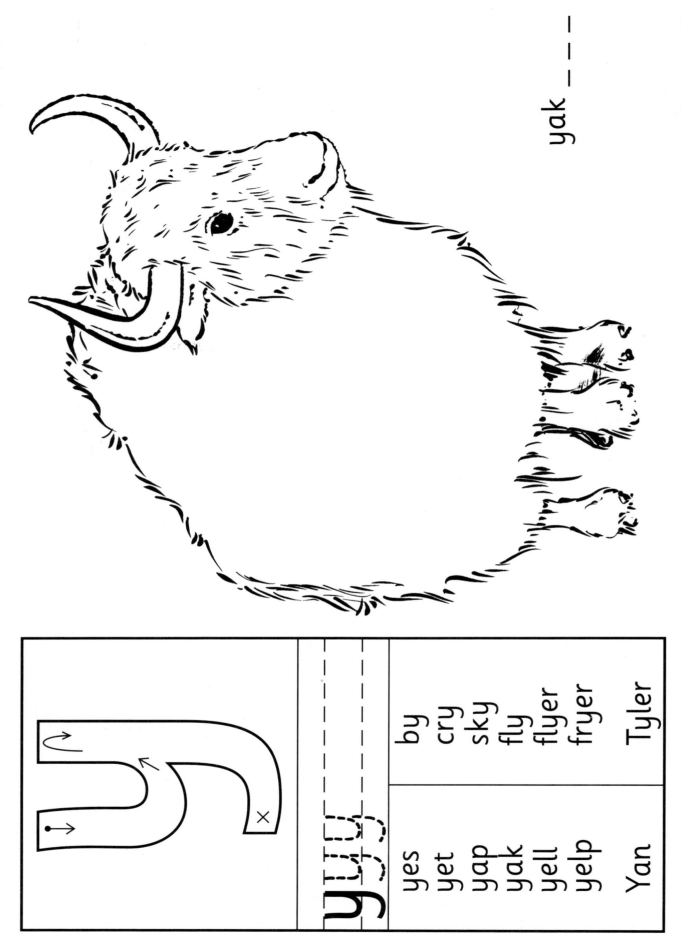

y y y

yes
yet
yap
yak
yell
yelp

Yan

by
cry
sky
fly
flyer
fryer

Tyler

yak – – –

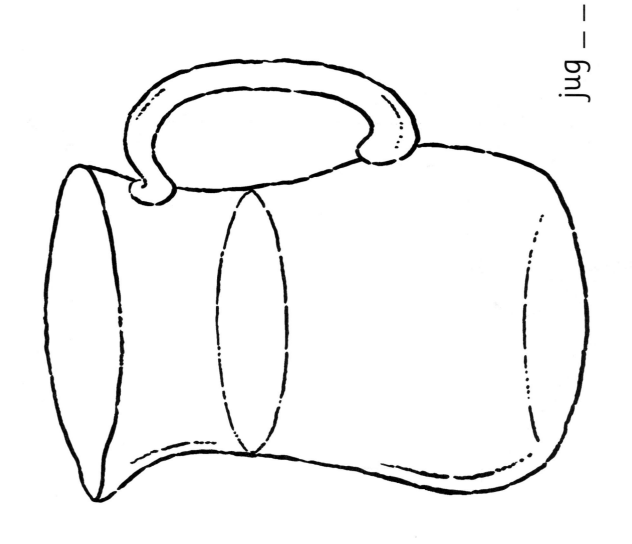

jug _ _ _

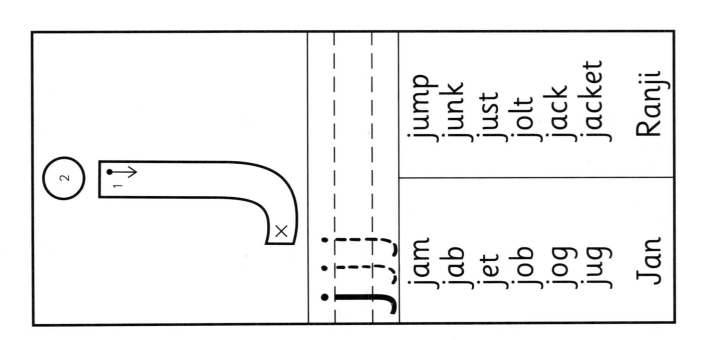

2

j j j

jam	jump
jab	junk
jet	just
job	jolt
jog	jack
jug	jacket
Jan	Ranji

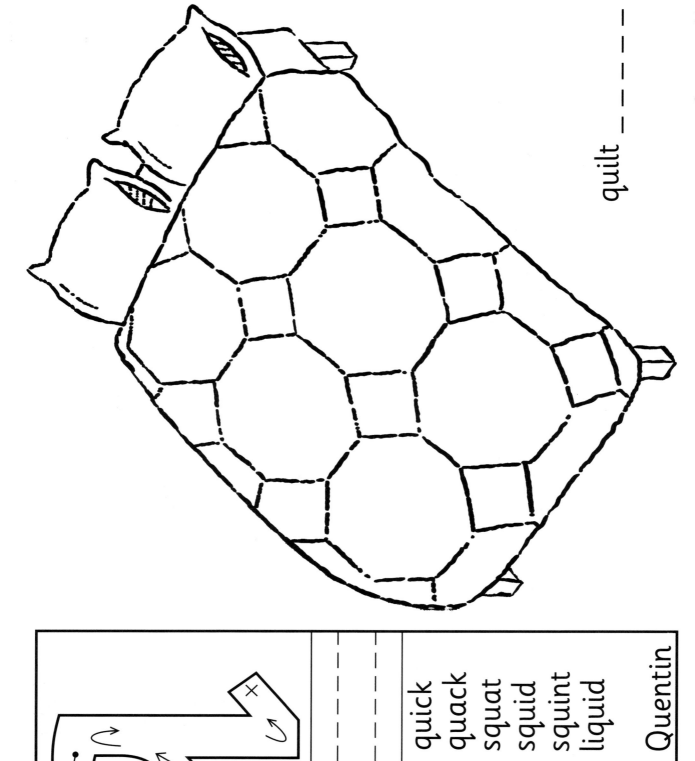

q q q

qid   quick
quit   quack
quiz   squat
quins   squid
quell   squint
quilt   liquid

Queen   Quentin

quilt — — — —

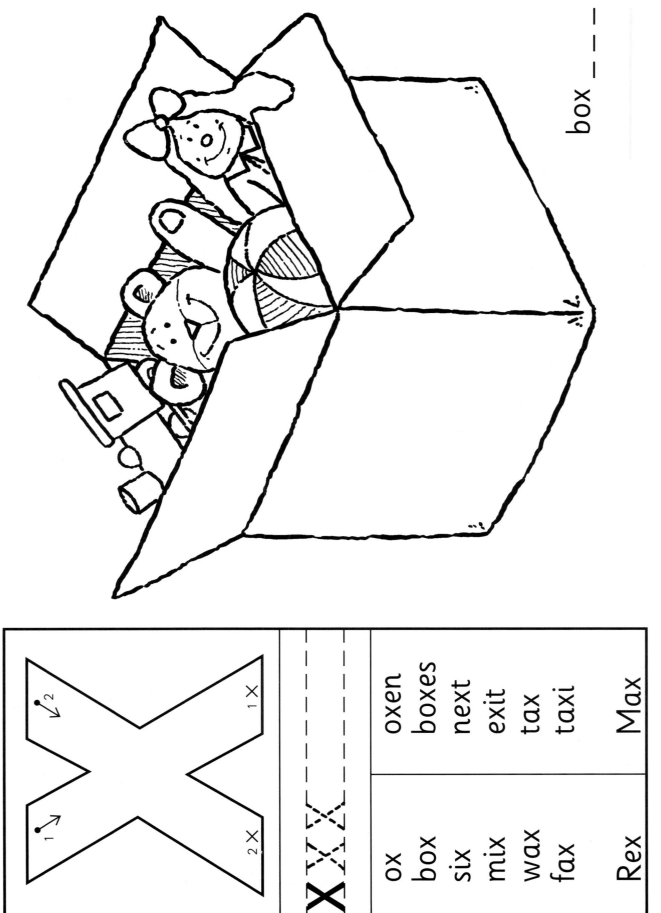

X

ox   oxen
box   boxes
six   next
mix   exit
wax   tax
fax   taxi

Rex   Max

box _ _ _

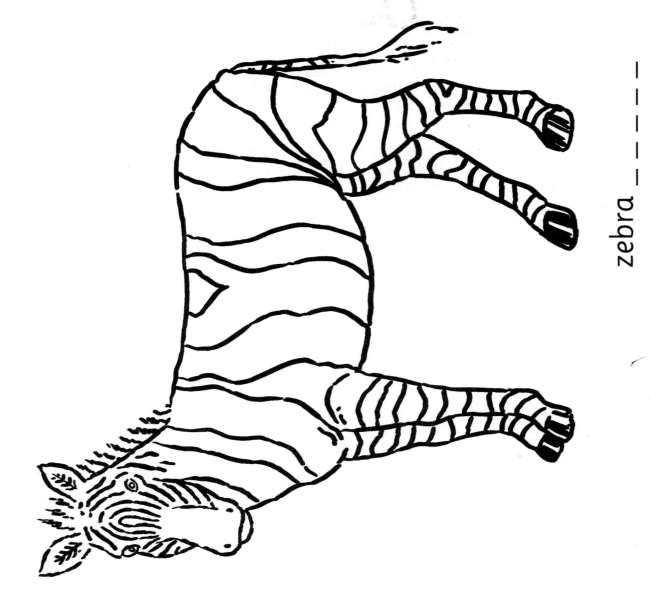

Z

z z z

zip	buzz
zed	fuzz
zap	fizz
zig	fizzy
zag	lazy
zoo	crazy
Zen	Liz

zebra

SECTION 2

GAMES AND ACTIVITIES FOR SINGLE SOUNDS AND SIMPLE BLENDING

C27 –34

These copymaster sheets draw together the work of Section 1 through activities.

Copymasters 27 and 28
Children point to the picture, say what it is and the sound the word begins with. Next they point to the letter beside it and say the sound. They then circle any letter, along the line, which is the same, saying the sound as they circle the letter.

Copymasters 29, 30 and 31
Colour in the copymaster colour chart in Section 10 and display it prior to this task. Go through it with the children so that they can use the chart for reference for this and succeeding tasks.

Children colour the picture in the strip with the colour alongside. They then colour the shapes containing the initial sound of the word depicted. For example, they colour the mug pink then all the stars with 'm' in them, the nut brown and all the stars with 'n' in them.

This allows easy checking of the children's progress.

Copymaster 32
Children say the name of the item in the picture, listen to the sounds they hear, and then write down the word:

cup, peg, sun, mug, fox
mat (rug), pig, bed, ant, lid
leg, hen, rat, egg, ten

Copymaster 33
As above:

can, dog, cat, web, nut
bin, cap, pen, log, van
six, net, bun, hat, zip

Copymaster 34
Children should blend the letters to make each of the three words and then write down the two which are real words. Go through the completed work with the children and ask them if they can think of words which the 'non' words begin e.g. 'lem – lemon'.

Further activities for this level are in Section 9 and include Alphabet Sun, Alphabet Spiral, Stegosaurus, Sound Wheels, Find the Sound, Spinners and Ladders.

	d	d b h d k
	t	l t h k t
	r	n r m r i
	l	l t l k h l
	n	m n u v n
	s	s z c s e

	a	b c a o a
	e	o e c e a
	i	i j i l j
	o	o a o c e
	u	u n u v n

	c	o c a c e
	k	l h k d k
	g	p g q y g
	h	k h b h d
	y	g y q p y
	j	j y j f j g

✂ -

WELCOME	m	n m w m w
	p	b p d q p
	b	d q b p b
	f	l f k b f
	w	m n w u w
	v	w v m v u

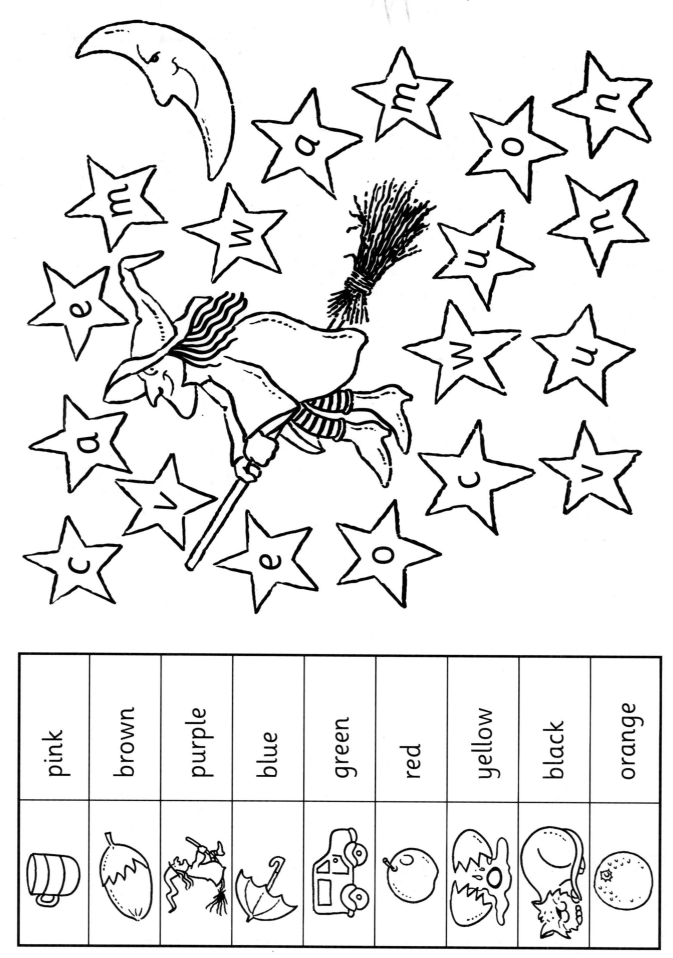

pink	
brown	
purple	
blue	
green	
red	
yellow	
black	
orange	

blue	
red	
pink	
yellow	
brown	
green	
purple	
black	

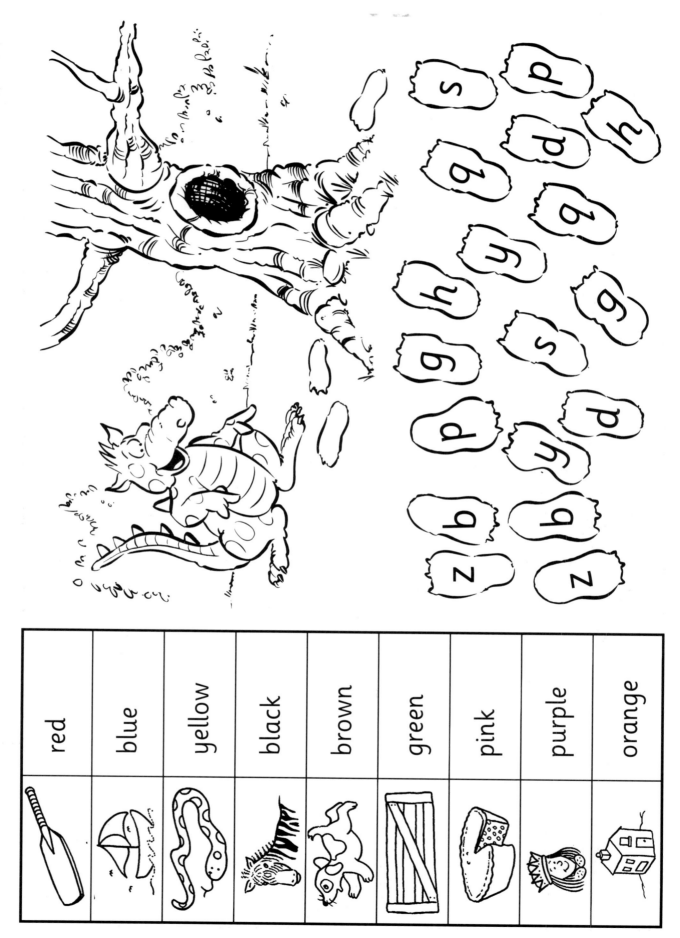

	red
	blue
	yellow
	black
	brown
	green
	pink
	purple
	orange

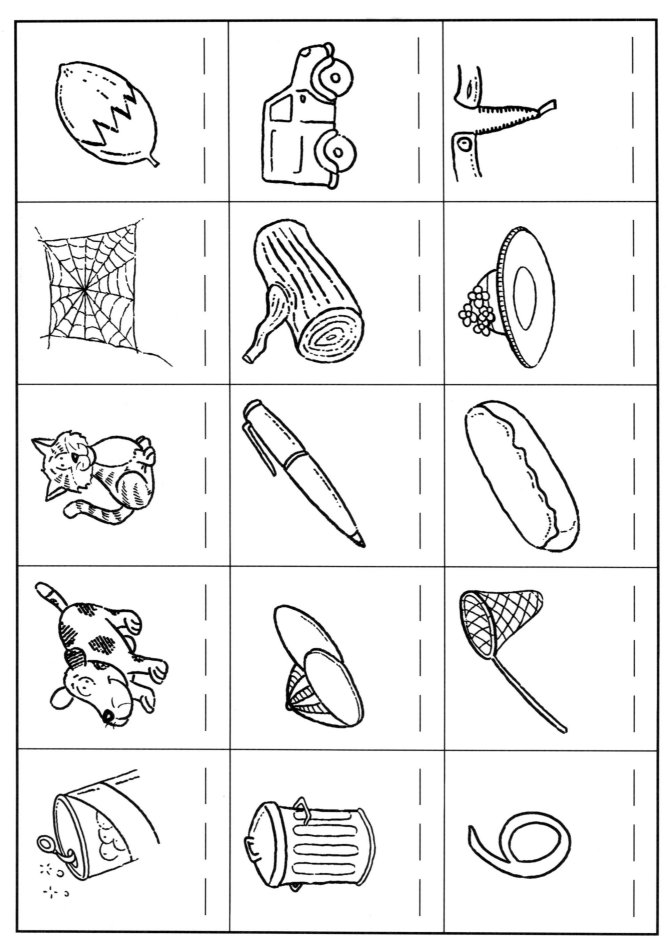

box mat mel		
ban cra top		
mus pin cat		
jam jal kit		
cut and lem		
bun nut sti		

✂ -

bat bri cut		
met tip spo		
ten fli not		
ste win yes		
nan sla rat		
flo van act		

SECTION 3

CONSONANT DIGRAPHS AND BLENDS

This section introduces forty-five of the most common consonant digraphs and blends. The pictures on each page are chosen with care so that they can be referred to and act as a reminder to the children of the sound they are working on.

1. Talk about the objects on the page and encourage children to identify the sound in common.
2. Point to the sound on the left. The children say the sound as they trace over the sound with the index finger of their writing hand several times.
3. Children say the sound as they write it in the spaces to complete one of the words on the picture. They sound the word and say each whole word several times before going on to the next one. Children should be encouraged to make as many words as they can and write them all down in the boxes e.g. on **Copymaster 39** the initial blends added to 'ip' make 'blip', 'clip', 'flip', and 'slip'. Children should select words from those they have made to write from memory.
4. Children study the shape of one of the completed words and then, turning the page over or folding back the strip of lines, write the word from memory saying the sounds of the word as they write it down. If the children can write more than one word at a time they should be encouraged to do so.
5. By turning back the page children can check the correctness of their response and identify any part of the word they may not have written correctly.

On **Copymaster 38** the top part has words with the voiced 'th' sound. The bottom part has useful look and say words beginning with the same sound. These words, often used in conjunction with those above, give problems so it was decided to include them. Encourage the children to make up phrases, orally, using the words in pairs e.g. then they …, with the ….

Several of the copymasters in this section show more than 12 words or illustrations. If the children are able to remember them all they can write their words two to a line.

Further activities for this section can be found in Sections 4 and 9.

sh

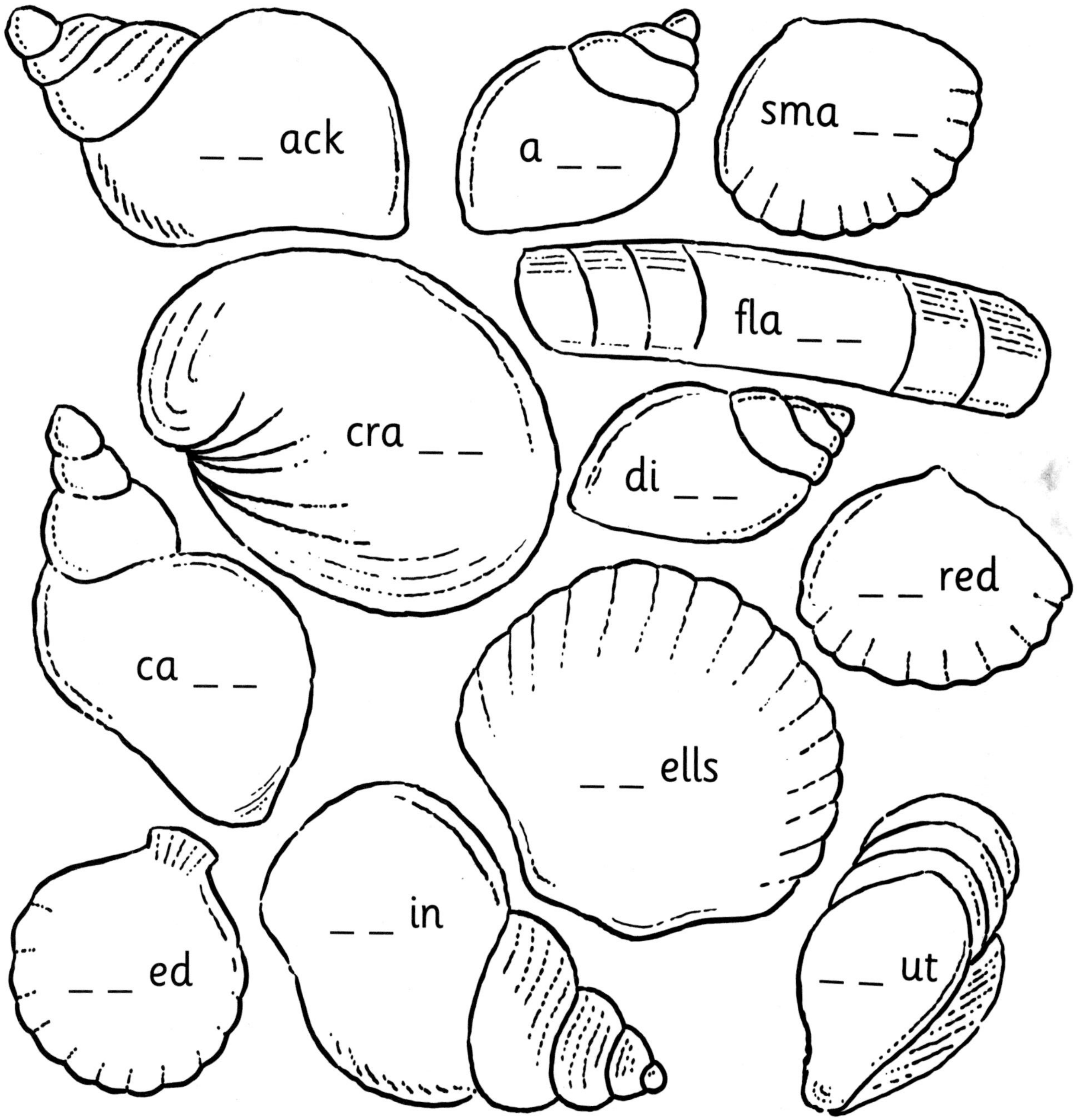

sma _ _

fla _

red _ _

ut _ _

a _ _

di _ _

ells
_ _ _

cra _ _

_ _ ack

ca _ _

in
_ _

ed
_ _

crun —— o

r ——
o

ill ——

ben —— o

in ——
o

mu ——
o
o

it ——

o
est ——

fin ——
o

ap
——

o
op ——

ick ——
o

ch

pi __

clo __

bro __

resh __

ud __

six __

__imble

eft __

rob __

in __

Smi __

pa __

th

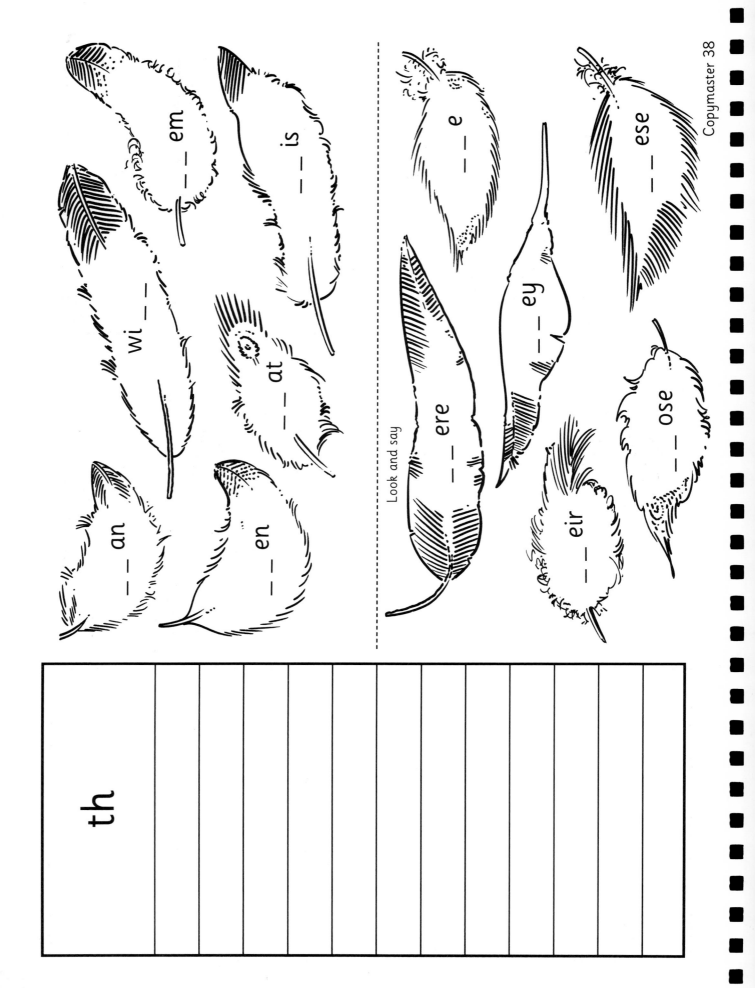

em

is

wi

at

an

en

e

ese

ey

ere

eir

ose

Look and say

th

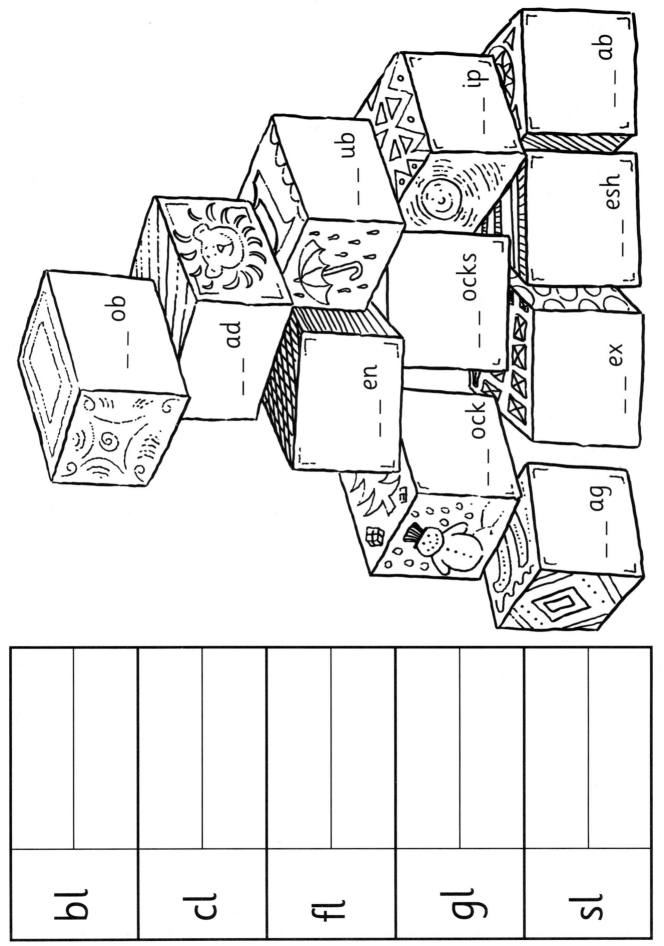

bl	
cl	
fl	
gl	
sl	

__ ob

__ ad

__ ub

__ en

__ ip

__ ocks

__ ock

__ ab

__ esh

__ ex

__ ag

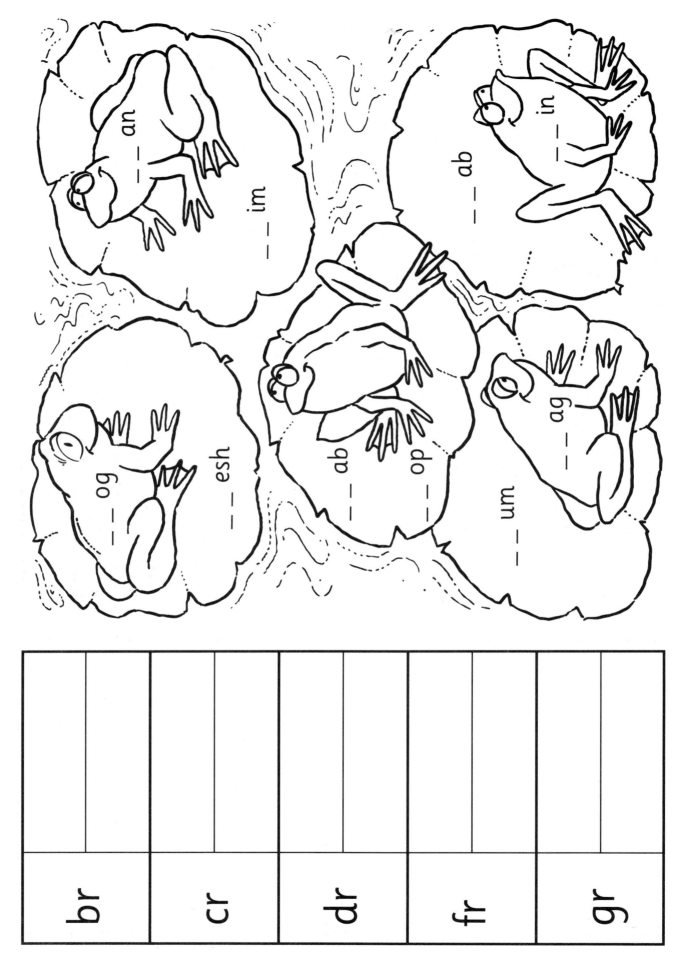

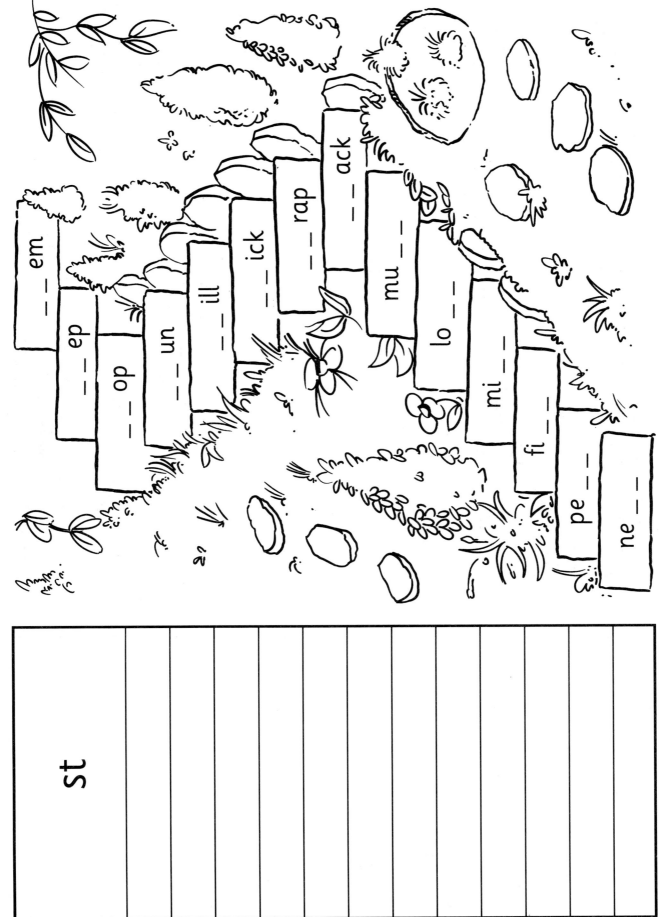

em
ep
op
un
ill
ick
rap
ack
mu
lo
mi
fi
pe
ne

st												

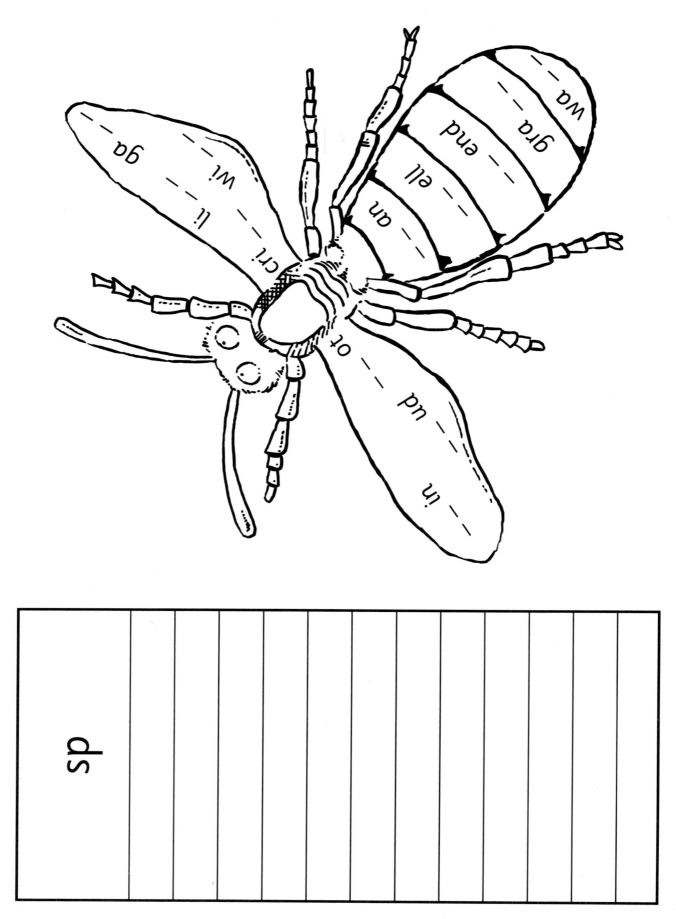

sp

ull

tu _ _

fla _ _

id

ma _ _

ta _ _

iff

ip _ _

bri _ _

de _ _

unk _ _

in _ _

sk

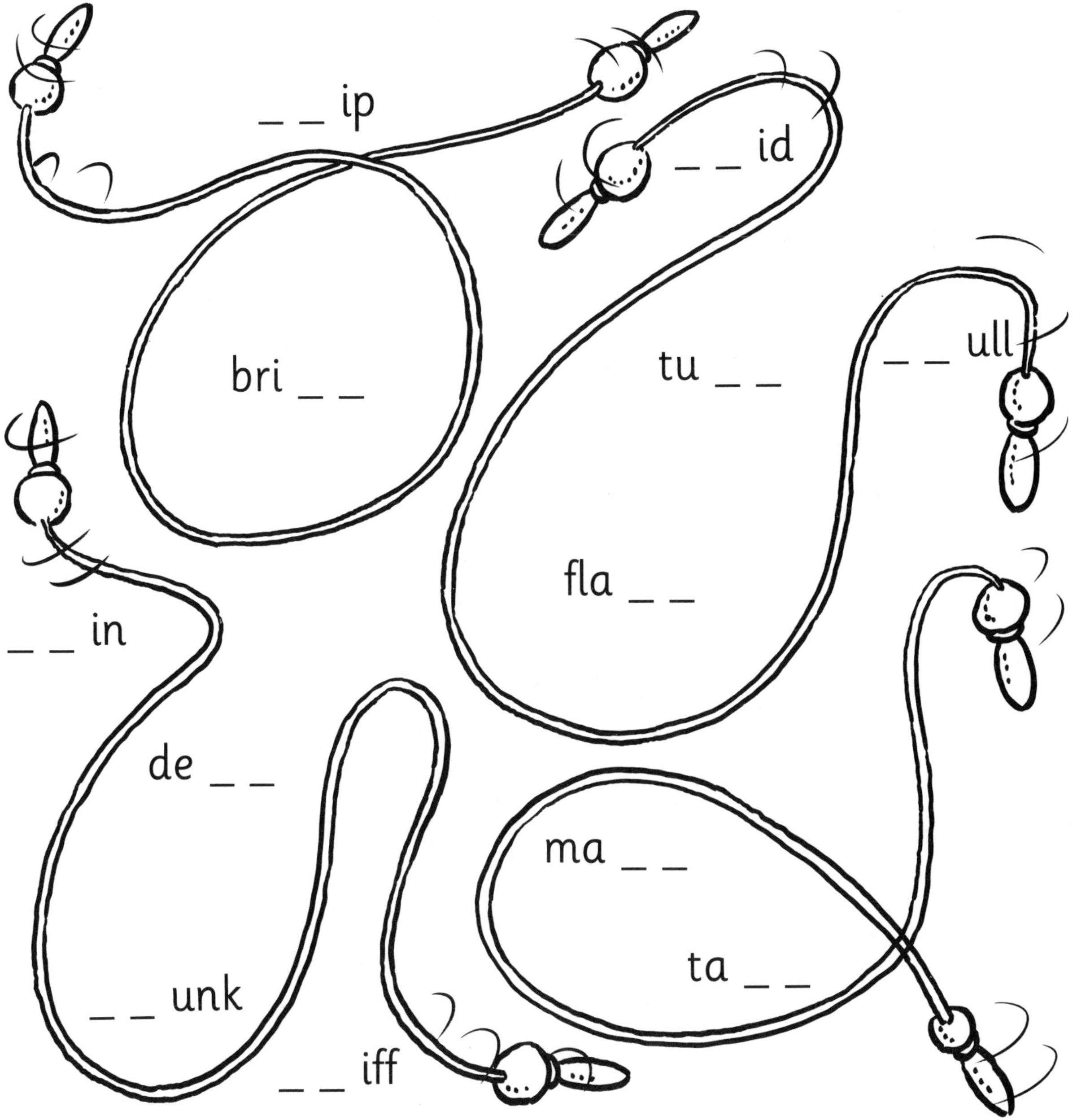

ith
alp
ab
ack
ash
ick
ip
uff
ug
ell
iff
an

sc sm sn

___ enty

___ elve

___ ish

___ ift

___ ig

___ in

___ itch

___ ist

___ an

___ ell

___ ept

___ im

___ amp

___ iss

sw	tw												

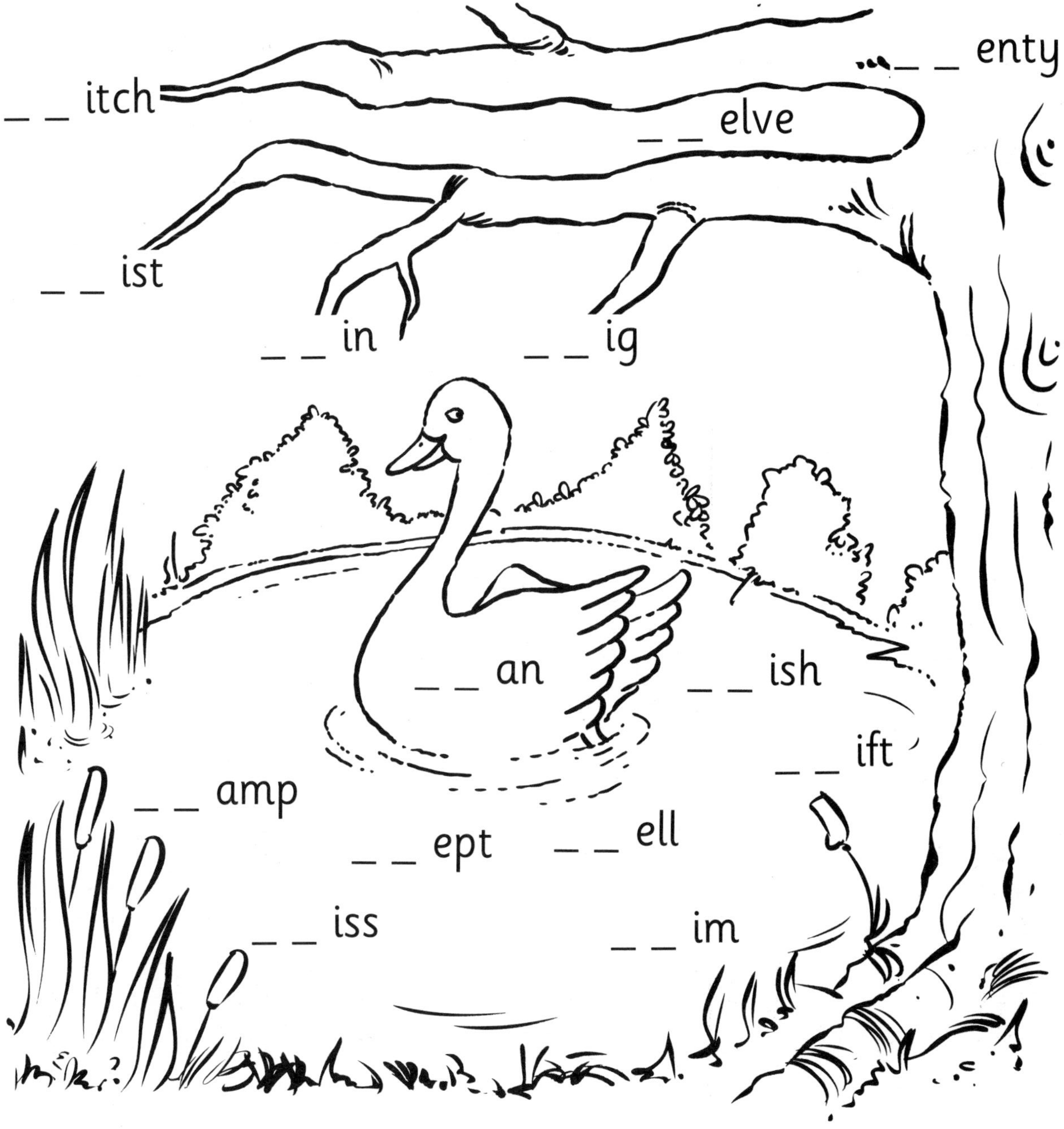

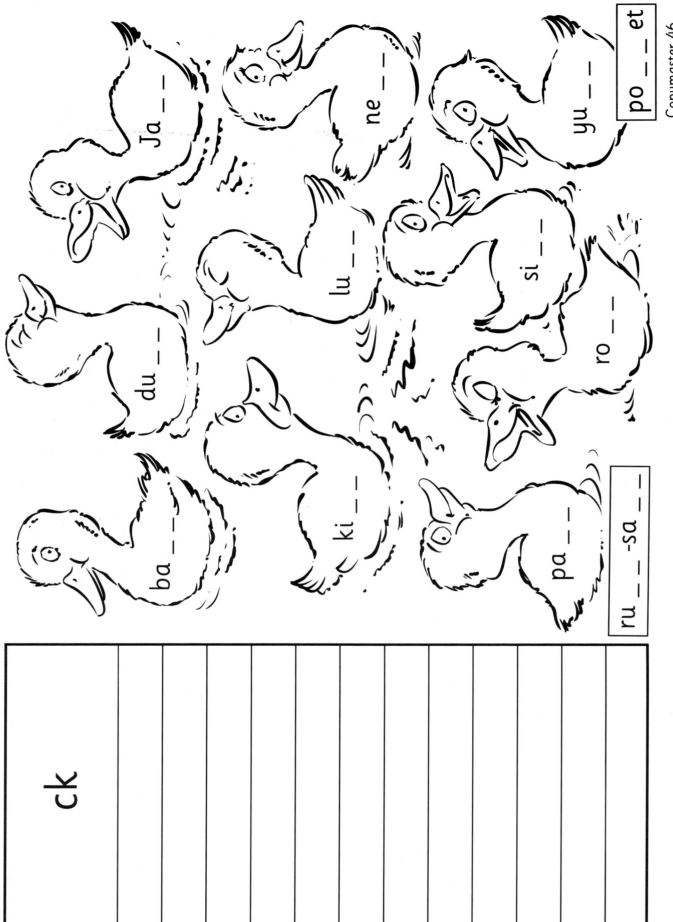

ba __ __

du __ __

ki __ __

Ja __ __

lu __ __

ne __ __

pa __ __

ru __ -sa __

si __ __

ro __ __

yu __ __

po __ __ et

ck

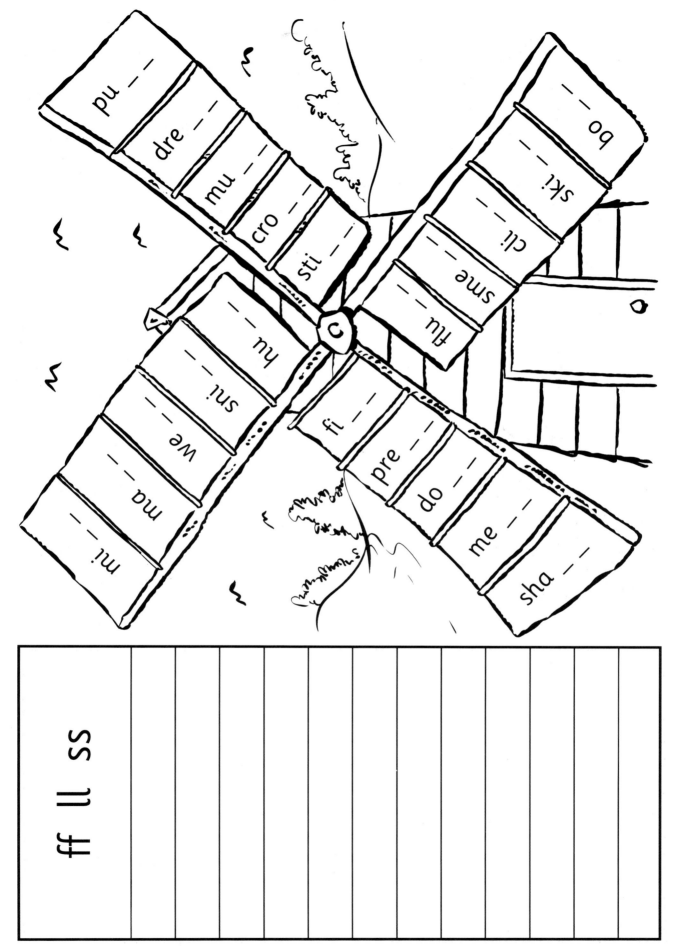

pu __
dre __
mu __
cro __
sti __

bo __
ski __
cli __
sme __
flu __

mi __
ma __
we __
sni __
nu __

fi __
pre __
do __
me __
sha __

ff   ll   ss

le

so

a

bo

me

fe

fa

gi

inb

pa

cra

tu

ct ft lt

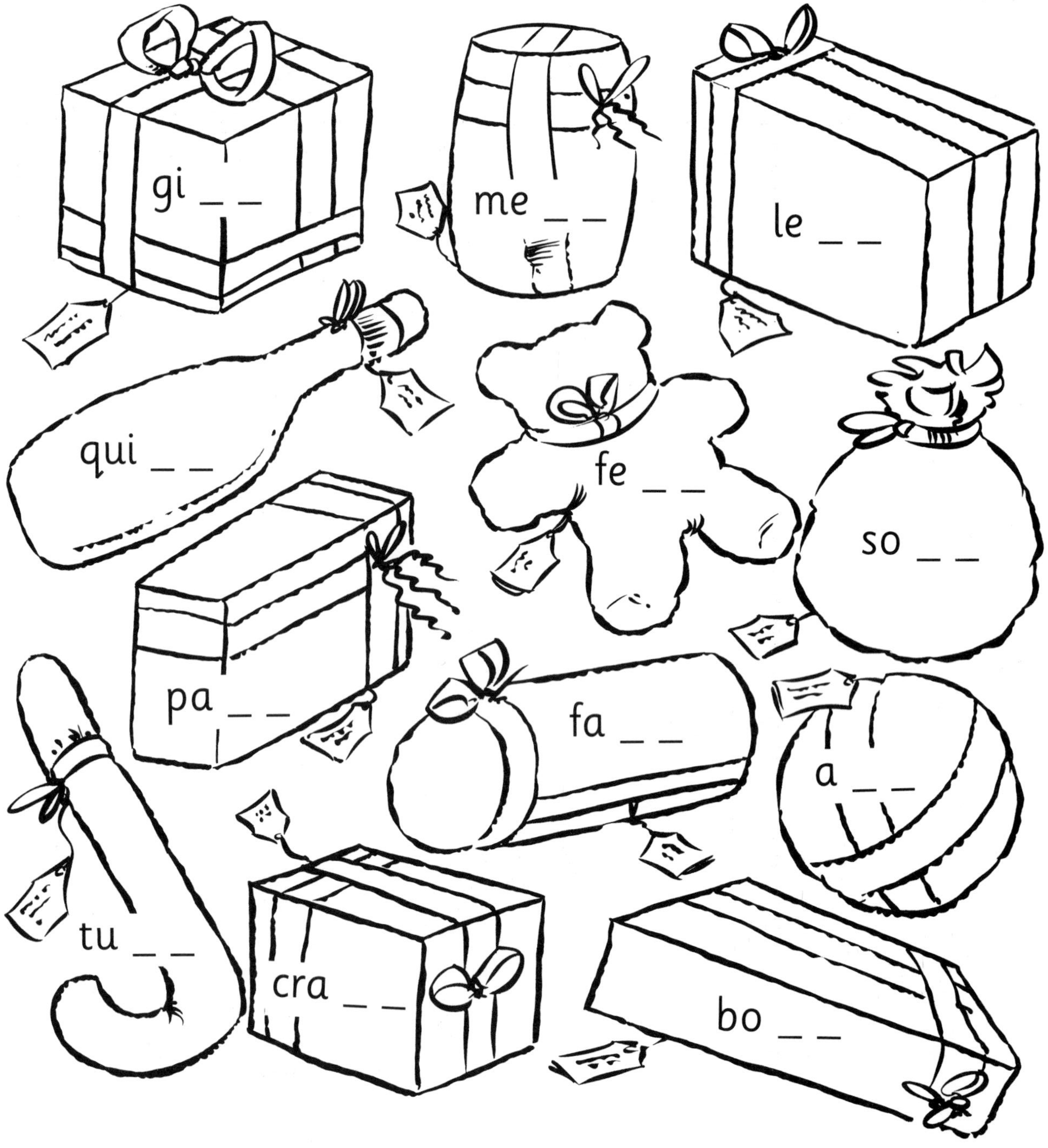

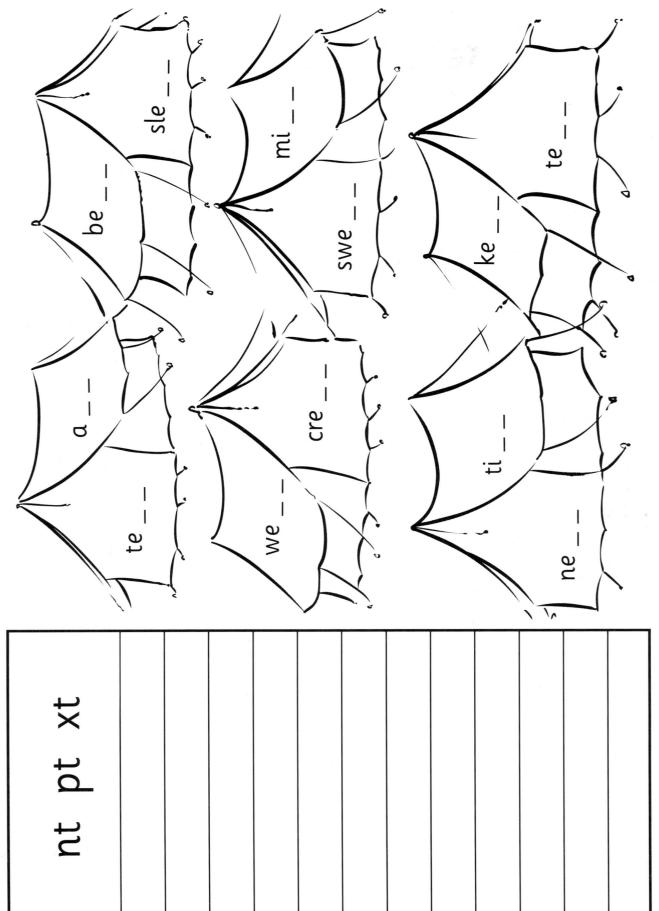

sle _ _
be _ _
mi _ _
swe _ _
te _ _
ke _ _
a _ _
cre _ _
we _ _
ti _ _
ne _ _

nt pt xt

fi _ _ | gu _ _ | si _ _ | he _ _

hy _ _ | e _ _ | ye _ _ | bu _ _

su _ _ | mi _ _ | y _ _ | pu _ _ | he _ _

lk lm lp

tch

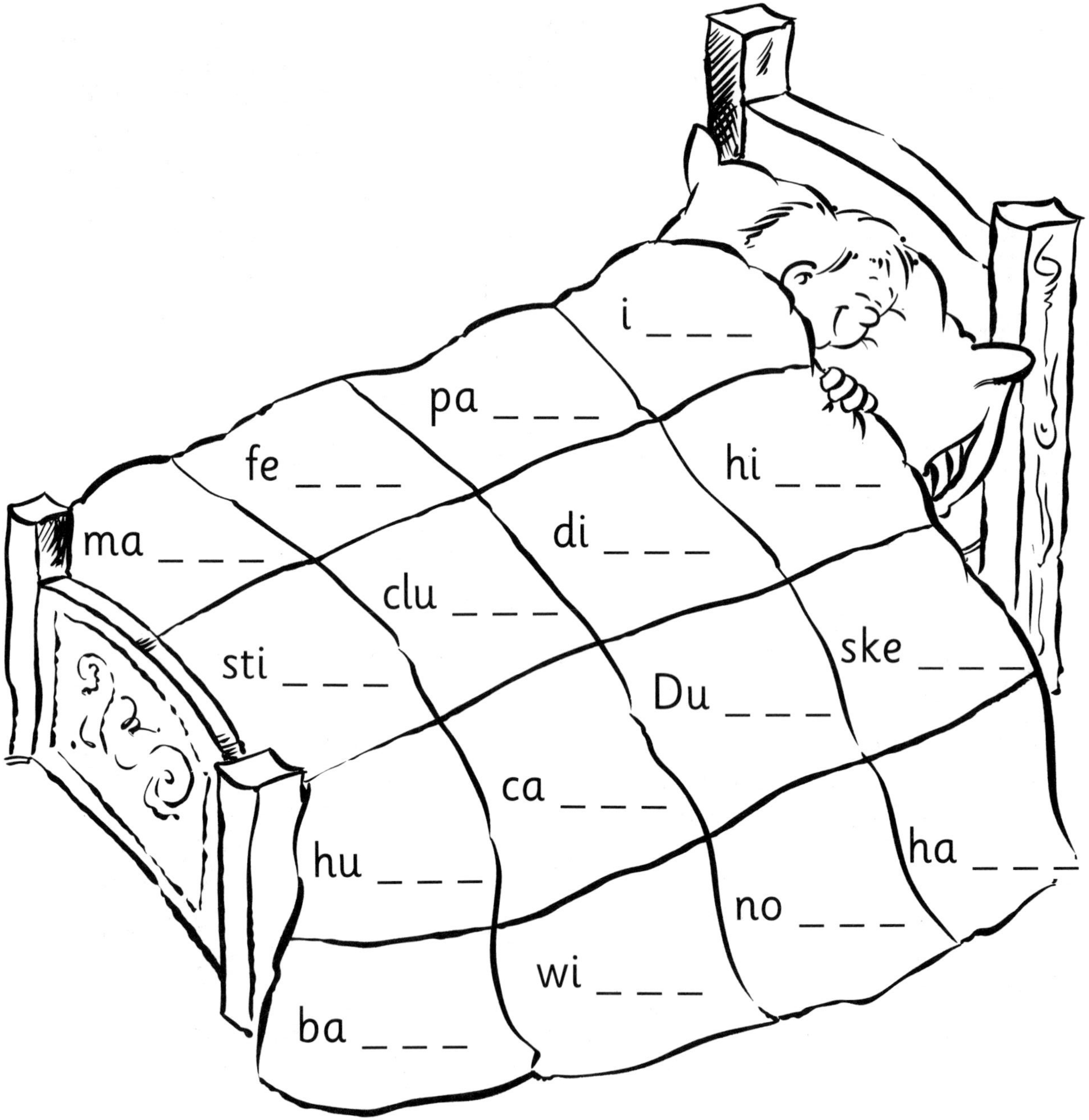

pa ___
hi ___
i ___
fe ___
di ___
clu ___
sti ___
ma ___
ske ___
Du ___
ca ___
hu ___
ha ___
no ___
wi ___
ba ___

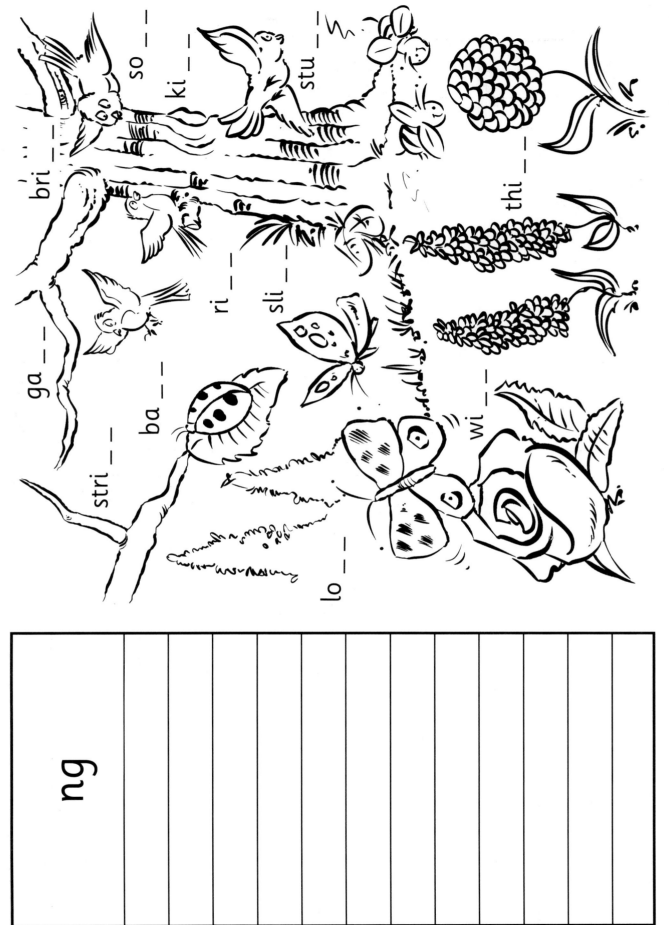

bri ___

so ___

ki ___

stu ___

ga ___

ri ___

thi ___

ba ___

sli ___

stri ___

wi ___

lo ___

ng									

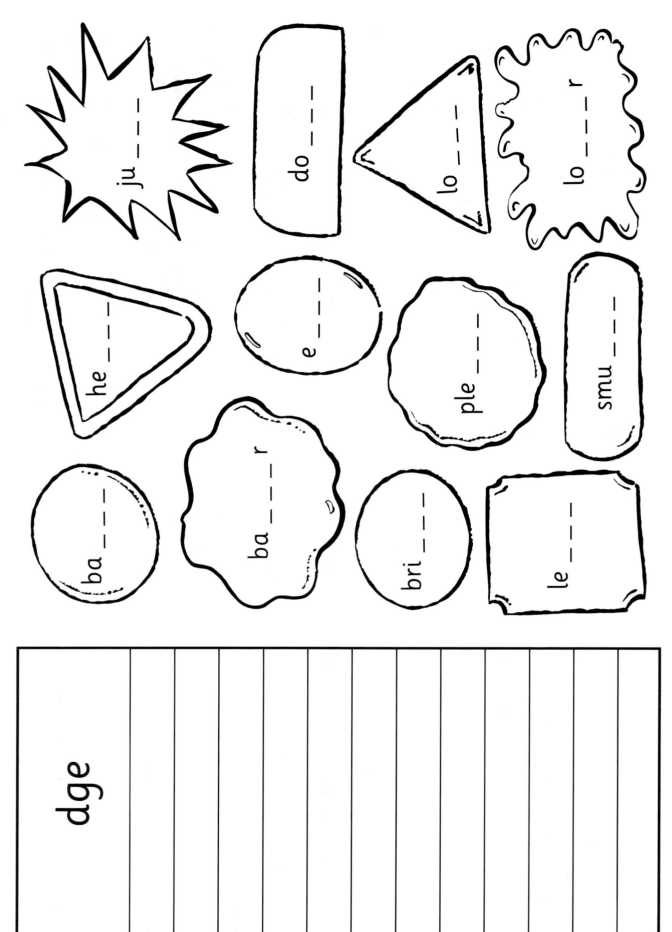

ju ___

do ___

lo ___

lo ___

he ___

e ___

ple ___

smu ___

ba ___

ba ___ r

bri ___

le ___

dge

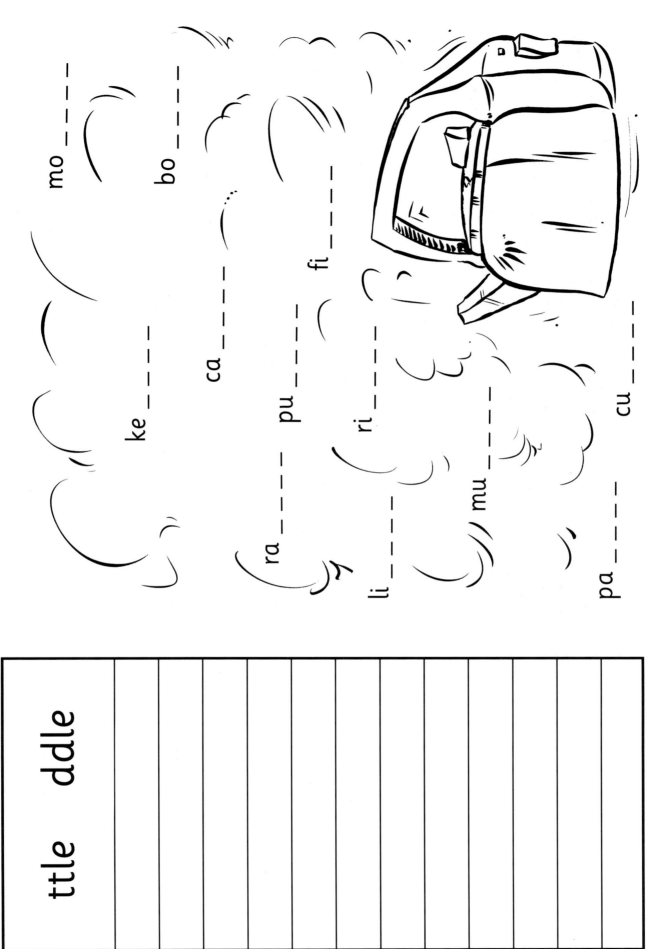

mo _ _ _

bo _ _ _

ke _ _ _

ca _ _ _

pu _ _ _

ra _ _ _

fi _ _ _

ri _ _ _

li _ _ _

mu _ _ _

pa _ _ _

cu _ _ _

ttle   ddle

fo _ _ _

ki _ _ _

a _ _ _

ta _ _ _ _

bu _ _ _

ha _ _ _

da _ _ _

ca _ _ _

recta _ _ _

si _ _ _ _

ji _ _ _ _

ju _ _ _

ndle ngle

SECTION 4

GAMES AND ACTIVITIES FOR CONSONANT DIGRAPHS AND BLENDS

These copymaster sheets draw together the work of Section 3.

Copymaster 57
Children say the name of the item in the picture, listen to the sounds they hear and then write down the word:

thimble, chick, bench, shop, fish
clock, blocks, frog, crab, steps
spots, skip, slug, swan, twig.

Copymaster 58
Worked as above:

duck, doll, rocks, quilt, tent
hedge, bank, pump, hutch, ring
film, candle, rattle, paddle, twinkle

Copymaster 59
Cut the lists in half vertically. Children read the sentence, build each of the three words at the end and circle the correct one for the picture. The children study the group of three words, fold over the picture strip, covering the three words, and try to write all three multiple choice words from memory. By lifting up the picture strip children use the list underneath to check

the correctness of their response. Some children may need to limit the numbers of words they write to two or one at a time, but encourage them to stretch themselves, they will gain confidence from so doing.

Copymaster 60
This sheet pulls together many of the sounds that the children have been working on. They study each little picture and fill in the missing consonant digraphs or blends.

Copymaster 61
Using their growing knowledge of single letter sounds and blends the children unjumble the letters to make words which describe the picture.

Copymaster 62
Cut the page in half vertically. Children cross out the non-words and, from those remaining, circle the matching pair. The page can be folded and the real words written in the box. The page can then be opened out so that the children can check their spellings against the original. If the children are not sure whether the word is a real one or not, show them how to check it in a dictionary.

73

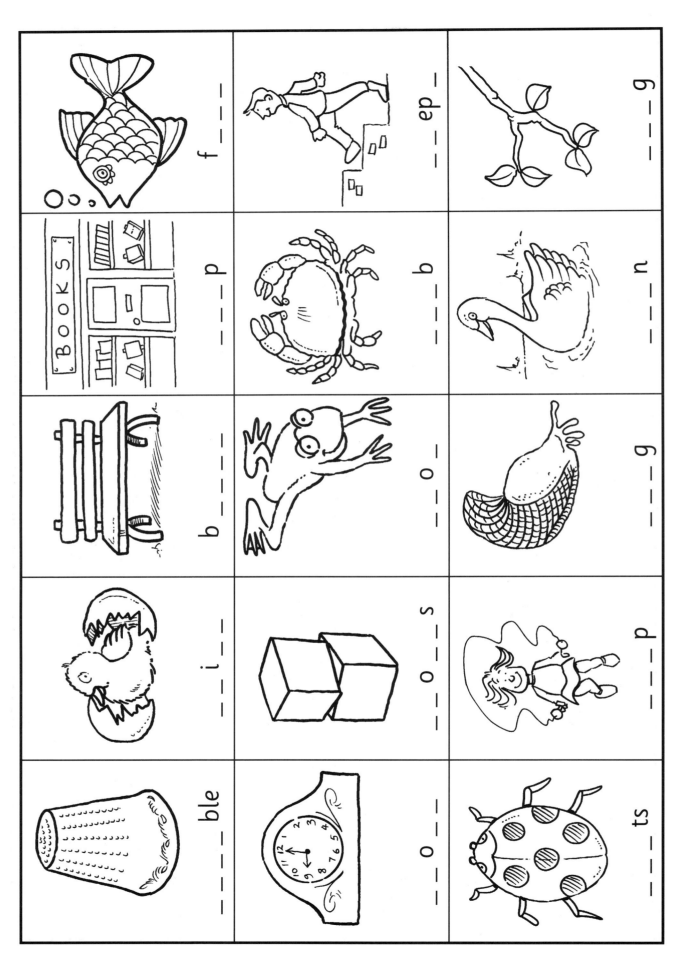

f _ _ | _ _ _ ep | _ _ _ g

_ _ p | _ _ b | _ _ n

_ _ b | _ _ o | _ _ g

_ i _ | _ o _ s | _ _ p

_ _ _ ble | _ o _ | _ _ ts

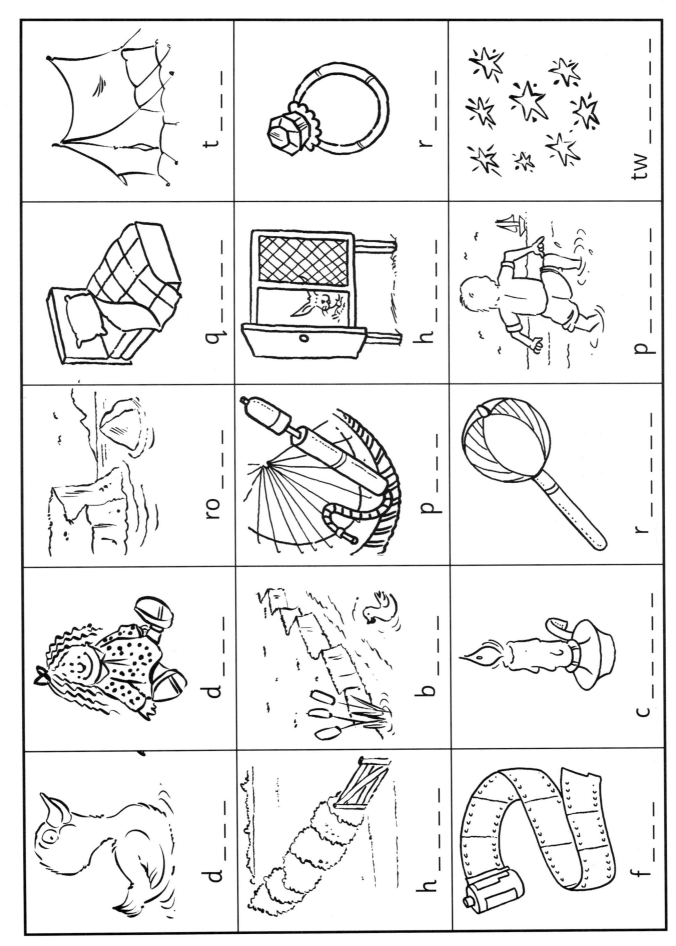

t _ _ _

b _ _ _

ro _ _ _

d _ _ _

p _ _ _

r _ _ _

h _ _ _

p _ _ _

b _ _ _

h _ _ _

tw _ _ _

p _ _ _

r _ _ _

c _ _ _

f _ _ _

Clem held the   clan   flag   flog

Greg picks up a   grab   cram   crab

Skip has on a   mast   task   mask

Cliff went up to the   mill   moll   will

The left is shut   gift   lift

Ross swift the   spelt   swing   string   swept   spring

Josh went to the   ship   shop   chop

Trish had six   dishes   wishes   fishes

Chad sat on the   lunch   bunch   bench

Beth fell with a   hump   thump   lump

Mick fed the   decks   backs   ducks

Stan went up the   stops   straps   steps

_ _ i _

co _ _ erel

_ a _ _

a _ _ ee

mi _ _ ing
_ _ ed

pig _ _ y

bu _ _

ca _ _ _ _

_ _ ade

_ a _ _ or

du _ _ s

he _ _

mi _ _

po _ _

_ _ eep

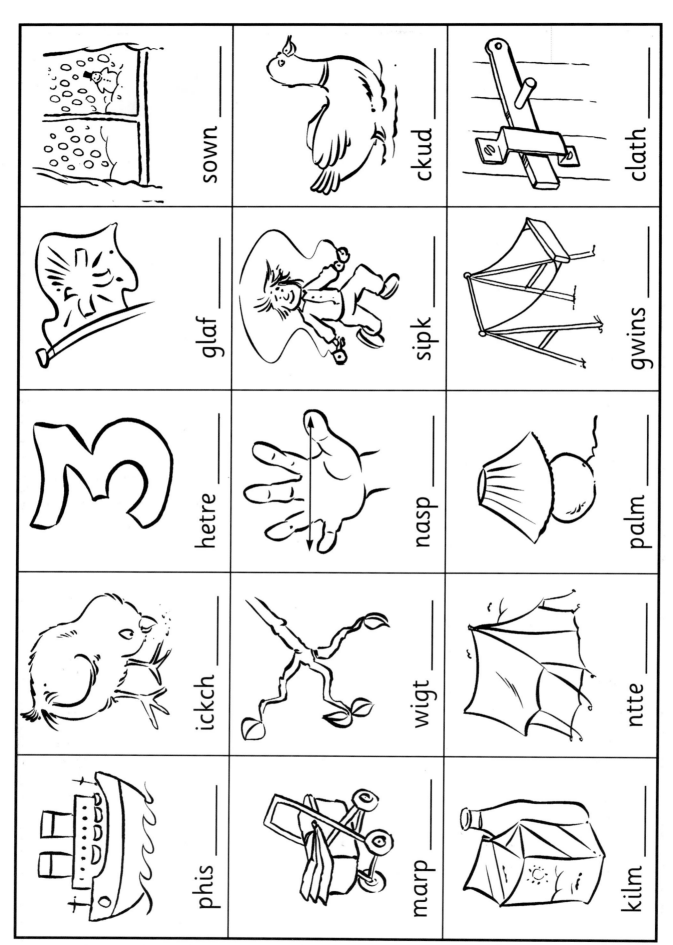

sown ____

ckud ____

clath ____

glaf ____

sipk ____

gwins ____

hetre ____

nasp ____

palm ____

ickch ____

wigt ____

ntte ____

phis ____

marp ____

kilm ____

gitf gift figt gjft gift	flap plag flag galf flag
caft tacf fact tcaf fact	spil slip plis slip slup
nett tent tnet tint tent	blue club culb clud club
pekt tept kept petk kept	drap brop drop prod drop
mift film milf fiml film	gorf frog forg grof frog
pleh leph help halp help	brag grab barg grab garb

SECTION 5

VOWEL DIGRAPHS AND BLENDS

This section introduces 28 common vowel digraphs and double vowel sounds. In order to introduce as many sounds as possible within the space allowed there are two sounds on each sheet. Please cut each page in half so that children work on one sound at a time. Similar sounds are paired for your convenience but it would confuse a child to be working on, say 'ea' and 'ee' at the same time.

The pictures on the pages are chosen with care so that they can be referred to and act as a reminder to the children of the sound they are working on.

1. Talk about the object or objects on the page and encourage children to identify the sound in common.
2. The children find the sound on the page and say the sound.

3. Children say the sound as they write it in the spaces to complete one of the words on the picture. They sound the word and say each whole word several times before going on to the next one.
4. Children study the shape of one of the completed words and then turning the page over or folding back the strip of lines write the first word from memory saying the sounds of the word as they write it down. If the children can write more than one word at a time they should be encouraged to do so.
5. By turning back the page children can check the correctness of their response and identify any part of the word they may not have written correctly.

Further activities for this section can be found in Sections 6 and 9.

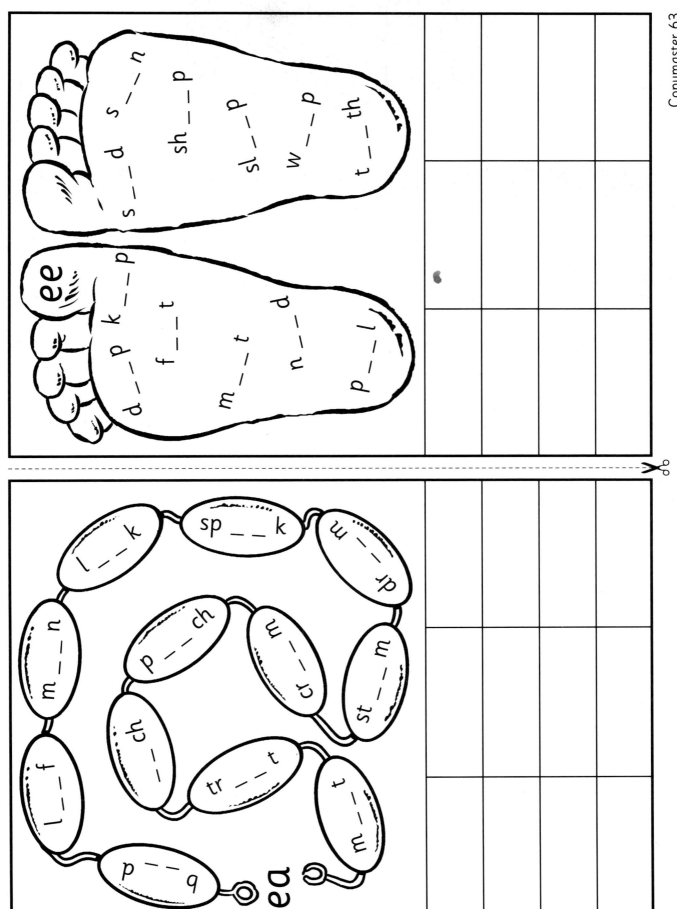

s _ n

s _ d   s _ p

sh _ p

sl _ p

w _ p

t _ th

ee

d _ p   k _ p

f _ _ t

m _ t

n _ d

p _ l

l _ _ k

sp _ _ _ k

dr _ _ m

m _ n

p _ _ ch

m _ _ cr

st _ _ m

l _ f

_ _ ch

tr _ _ t

m _ t

p _ _ q

ea

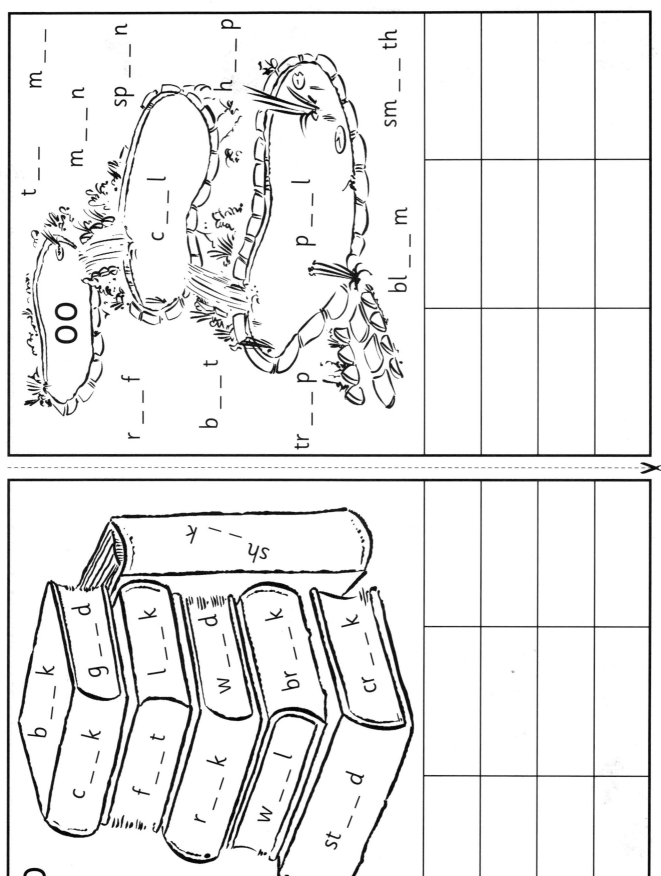

oo

t _ _ m
m _ _ n
sp _ _ n
c _ _ l
p _ _ l
h _ _ p
sm _ _ th
bl _ _ m
r _ _ f
b _ _ t
tr _ _ p
oo

oo

sh _ _ k
b _ _ k
c _ _ k
g _ _ d
f _ _ t
l _ _ k
r _ _ k
w _ _ d
w _ _ l
br _ _ k
st _ _ d
cr _ _ k

a-e

aw _ k

pl _ t _

t _

c _ m

b _ k

f _ d

l _ n _

m _ t _

sn _ k _

s _ m _

br _ v _

c _ v _

oa

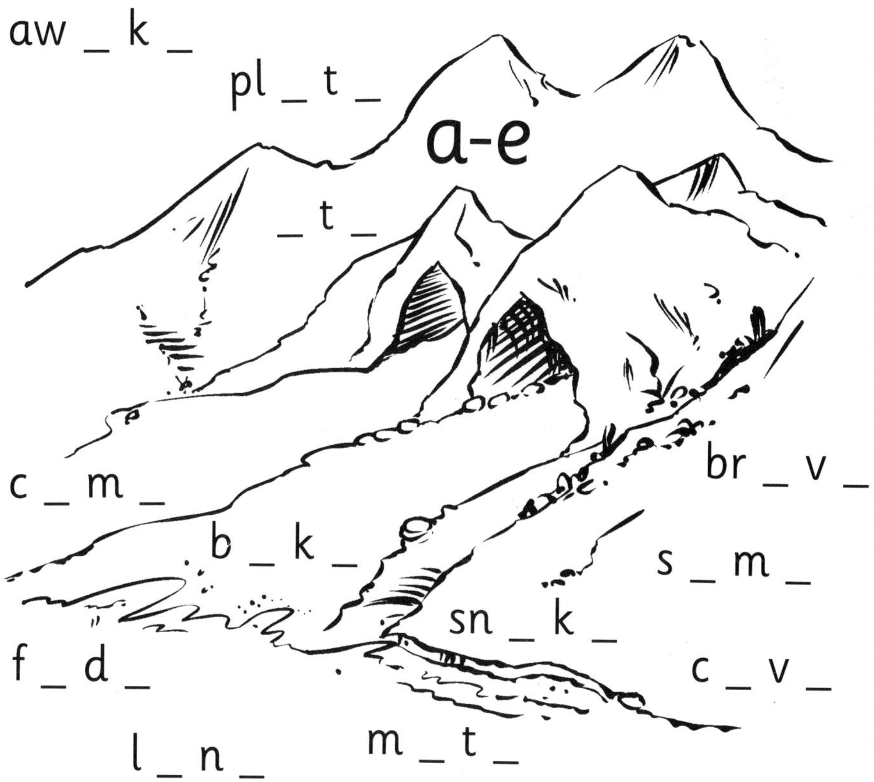

b _ t

c _ _ t

g _ _ t

l _ f

r _ m

f _ _ l

cr _ _ k

st

t _ _ t

_ _ k

r _ d

fl _ t

thr _ _ t

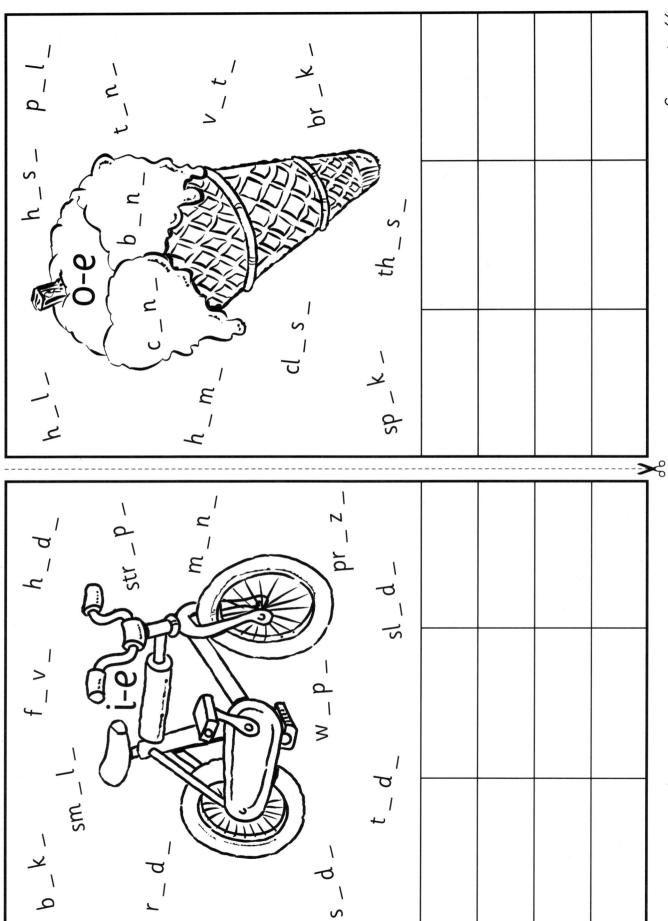

o-e

h_l_   h_s_   p_l_   t_n_

c_n_   b_n_   v_t_

h_m_   cl_s_   br_k_

sp_k_   th_s_

i-e

b_k_   f_v_   h_d_

sm_l_   str_p_   m_n_

r_d_   w_p_   pr_z_

s_d_   t_d_   sl_d_

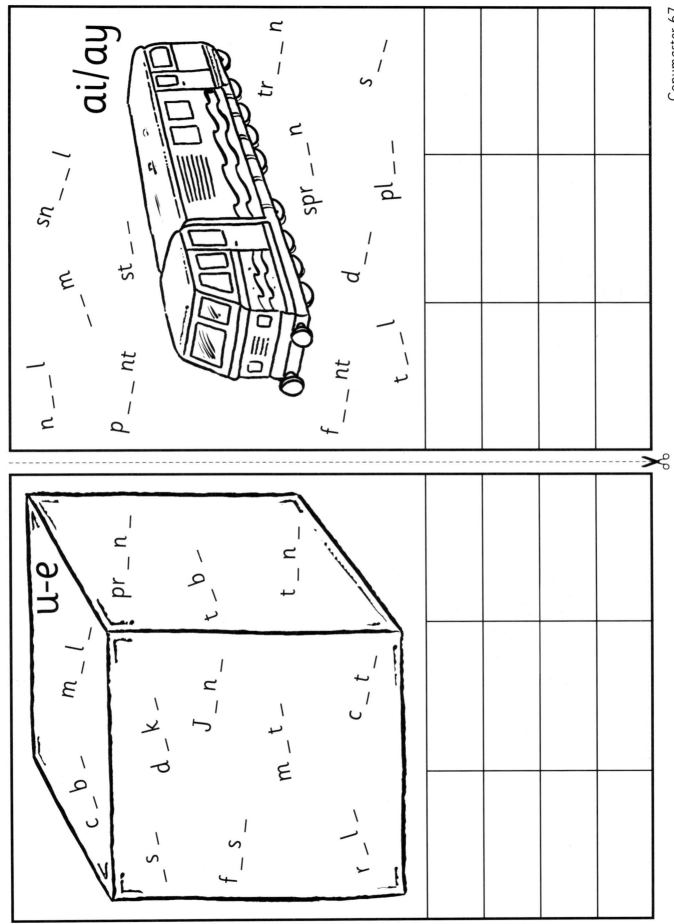

ai/ay

n __ l

sn __ l

__ m

st __

p __ nt

tr __ n

spr __ n

s __

d __

pl __

t __ l

f __ nt

u-e

c _ b _

m _ l _

pr _ n _

t _ b _

t _ n _

s _ _

d _ k _

J _ n _

m _ t _

c _ t _

f _ s _

r _ l _

ou

pr _ _ d   _ _ t   l _ _ d

sc _ _ t   p _ _ t

sn _ _ t   spr _ _ t   n _ _ n

m _ _ th   cl _ _ d

ab _ _ t   tr _ _ t

Toys & Games   oi/oy

p _ nt

s _ _ l

_ o

b _ _ l   c _ n

j _ _ n

m _ st   j _ st   c _ _ l

j _ _ t   b _ _

h _ _

OW

cl _ n

d _ n

c _ _

n _ _

l _ _

fr _ n

gr _ l

cr _ n

t _ n

br _ n

f _ l

sn _ _ man

wid _ _

sn _ _

thr _ _

ing

sh _ _

thr _ _

OW

cr _ _

gl _ _

gr _ _

fl _ _

l _ _

dr __ __

gr __ __

st __ __

bl __ __

scr __ __

f __ __

ch __ __

d __ __

m __ __

fl __ __

shr __ __

cr __ __

ew

y __ n

l __ __

r __ __

h __ __ k

d __ n

j __ __

sh __ __ l

pr __ n

spr __ l

str __ __

p __ __

f __ n

aw

er

t _ _ m   h _ _ m   h _ _ h   h _ _ b   v _ _ b

f _ _ n   h _ _ d

k _ _ b   c _ _ h   st _ _ n   g _ _ m

j _ _ k   p _ _ ch   p _ _ m

ar

m _ _ ch   t _ _ t   m _ _ h   f _ _ t   c _ _ t

sc _ _ f   k _ _ b   k _ _ k

sh _ _ k   k _ _ d

sm _ _ t   c _ _ t

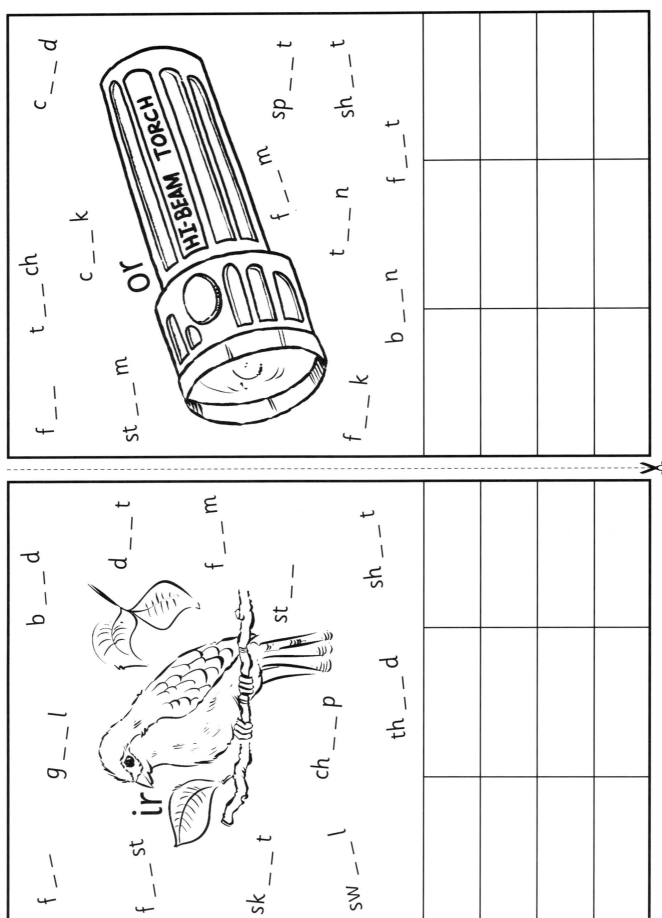

or

HI-BEAM TORCH

f _ _
t _ _ch
st _ _ m
c _ _ k
c _ _ d

f _ m
t _ n
b _ n
sp _ t
sh _ t
f _ t
f _ k

ir

f _ _
g _ l
f _ st
sk _ t
sw _ l
b _ d
d _ t
ch _ p
f _ m
st _ _
th _ _ d
sh _ _ t

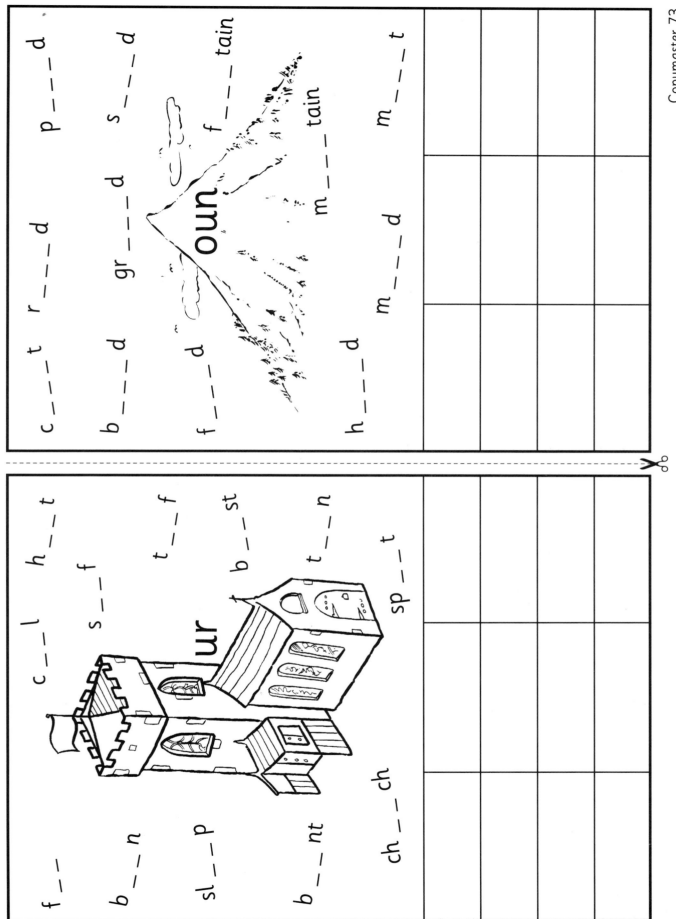

p _ _ d

t r _ _ d

c _ _ _ d

s _ _ d

gr _ _ d

b _ _ d

oun

f _ _ d

f _ _ tain

_ _ tain

m _ _ tain

m _ _ d

h _ _ d

m _ _ t

c _ _ l

h _ _ t

s _ _ f

t _ _ f

b _ st

ur

t _ _ n

f _ _ _

b _ _ n

sl _ _ p

ch _ _ ch

b _ _ nt

sp _ _ t

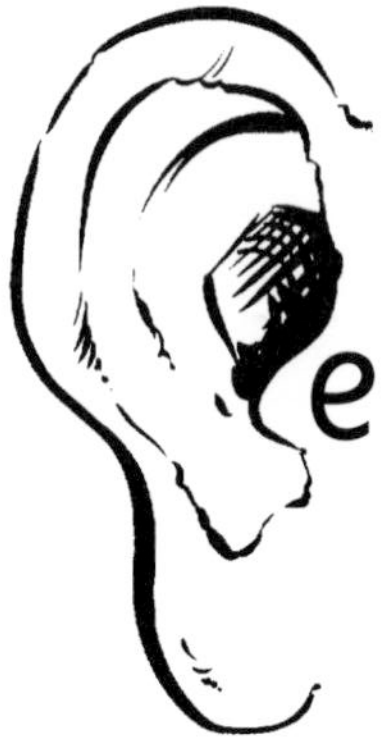

ear

d _ _ _

g _ _ _

_ _ _

sh _ _ _

n _ _ _

f _ _ _

sm _ _ _

y _ _ _

sp _ _ _

h _ _ _

b _ _ _ d

cl _ _ _

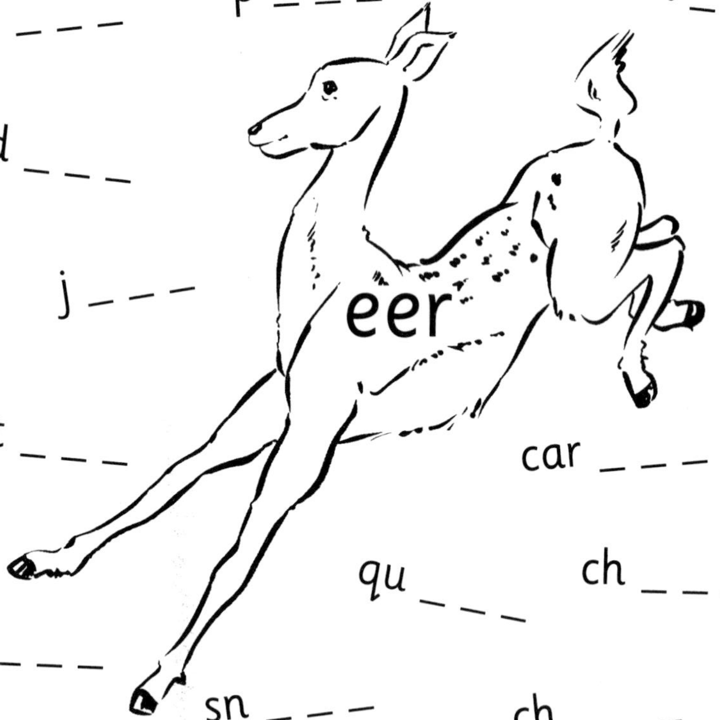

eer

b _ _ _

p _ _ _

sh _ _ _

d _ _ _

j _ _ _

st _ _ _

car _ _ _

qu _ _ _

ch _ _ _ y

v _ _ _

sn _ _ _

ch _ _ _

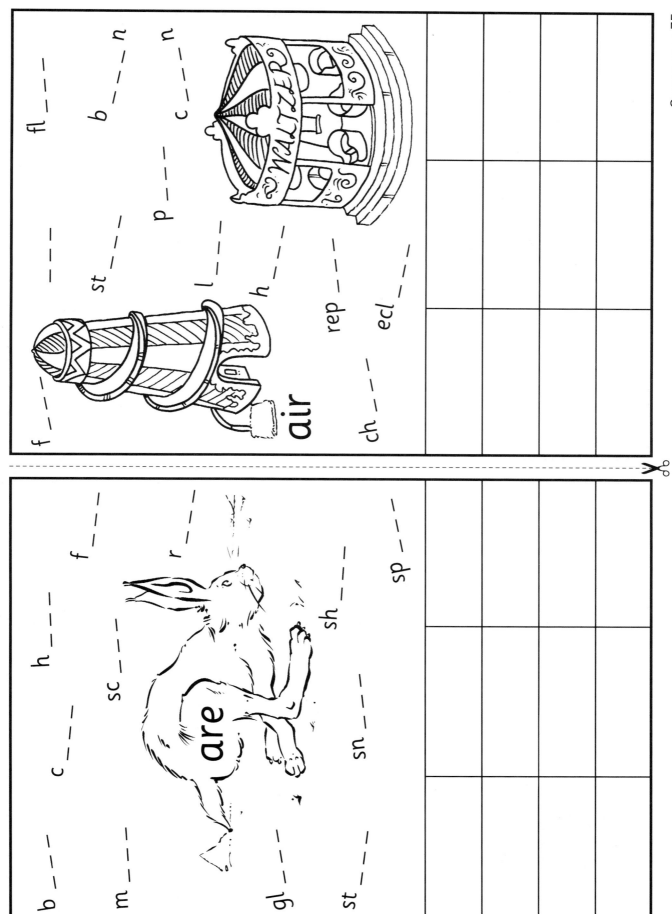

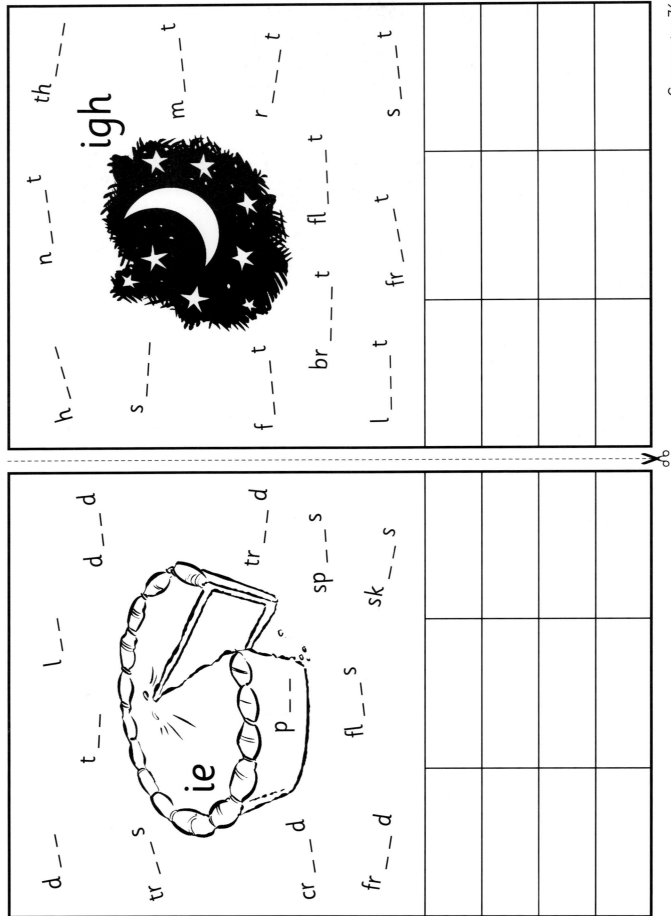

igh

th _ _ t
n _ _ t
m _ _ t
r _ _ t
h _ _ _
s _ _ t
f _ _ t
s _ _ t
br _ _ t
fl _ _ t
fr _ _ t
l _ _ t

ie

d _ _ _
l _ _
d _ _ d
t _ _ _
tr _ _ d
tr _ _ s
p _ _ _
sp _ _ s
cr _ _ d
fl _ _ s
sk _ _ s
fr _ _ d

SECTION 6

These copymaster sheets draw together the work of Section 5 by using games and activities.

Copymaster 77
Vowel digraphs and blends are used to complete the 'sound' words:

roar, moo, croak, bleat,
tweet, hoot, meow, squeak,
growl, bark, cheep, speak.

Copymaster 78
Cut the page in half along the dotted line. The non-words are crossed out and from those remaining the children circle the matching pair. The page can be folded over and the real words written in the box from memory. The page can then be opened out so that the children can check their spellings against the typed ones.

Copymaster 79
Children complete the sentences below the pictures by selecting from the words given.

Copymaster 80
In the gift boxes, the children should list as many words as they can with the same letter string.

Copymaster 81
Children fill in the blanks to complete the words in the two nursery rhymes. Make sure the children have learnt these two nursery rhymes prior to work on this activity.

Copymaster 82
The initial letter of each illustrated sea-side word is given. Children are required to complete each word using the phonic knowledge they have gained from previous sections. Children can also put these words into sentences and read their writing to others, or to the class group, at the end of the session.

birds, book, sand-pies, sea weed,
pebbles, spade, sand castle, star fish,
waves, boats, light house, basket.

lambs bl _ _ t

mice squ _ _ k

but I sp _ _ k

frogs cr _ _ k

cats me _ _

chickens ch _ _ p

cows m _ _

owls h _ _ t

seals b _ _ k

lions r _ _ r

birds tw _ _ t

bears gr _ _ l

crown brown crwon nrowc crown	
stouc scout souct shout scout	
nrawp drawn prawn pwarn prawn	
fried dries fries freid fried	
nuord round rounb round sound	
chew blew dlew blwe blew	
sight right rigth bright right	

✂

baed bead dear bedb bead	
peek kolp keep kaal keep	
boak book koob bool book	
coot coat caot coal coat	
jion join joint join groin	
raid rain rian rain pain	
fort frot forth fort trof	

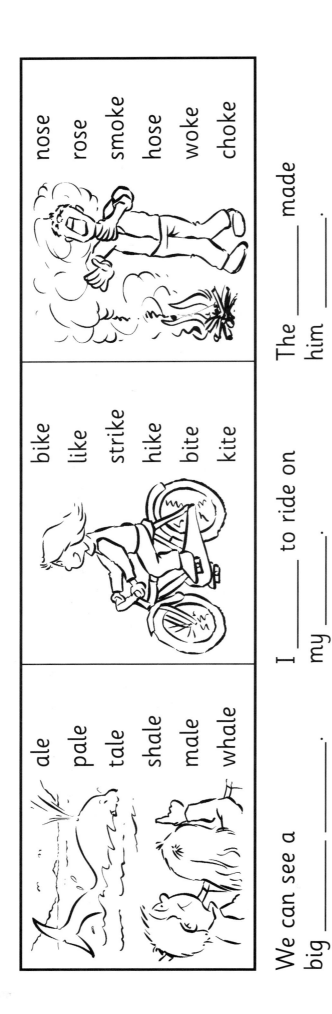

nose
rose
smoke
hose
woke
choke

bike
like
strike
hike
bite
kite

ale
pale
tale
shale
male
whale

The _____ made him _____.

I _____ to ride on my _____.

We can see a big _____.

rain
train
stain
chain
pain
paint

lout
snout
shout
pound
ground
found

fur
burn
turn
curl
turtle
hurt

He went on the _____ just before the _____.

They _____ a _____ on the _____.

My _____ came but I fell and _____ my leg.

Little Boy Blue

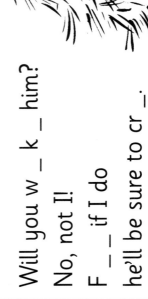

Little B_ _ Bl_ _ _

come bl_ _ your h_ _ n,

the sh_ _ p's in the m_ _ dow

the c_ _ _ 's in the c_ _ _ n.

Where's the b_ _

that l_ _ ks aft_ _ _ the sh_ _ _ p?

He's und_ _ _ _ the h_ _ stack

fast asl_ _ p.

Will you w_ _ k_ him?

No, not I!

F_ _ if I do

he'll be sure to cr_ _.

The Queen of Hearts

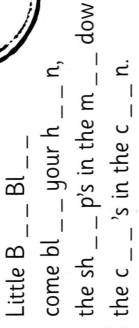

The Qu_ _ n of H_ _ _ _ ts

she m_ _ d_ some t_ _ _ts

all on a summ_ _ _ day.

The Kn_ _v_ of H_ _ _ _ ts

he st_ _l_ those t_ _ _ts

and quickly ran aw_ _ _.

The King of H_ _ _ _ ts

called for the t_ _ ts

and b_ _ _ t the Kn_ _v_ so s_ _ _ e

that Kn_ _v_ of H_ _ _ _ ts

brought back the t_ _ _ts

and s_ _ _ d he'd st_ _ _ l no m_ _ _ e.

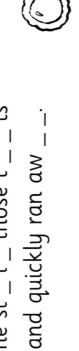

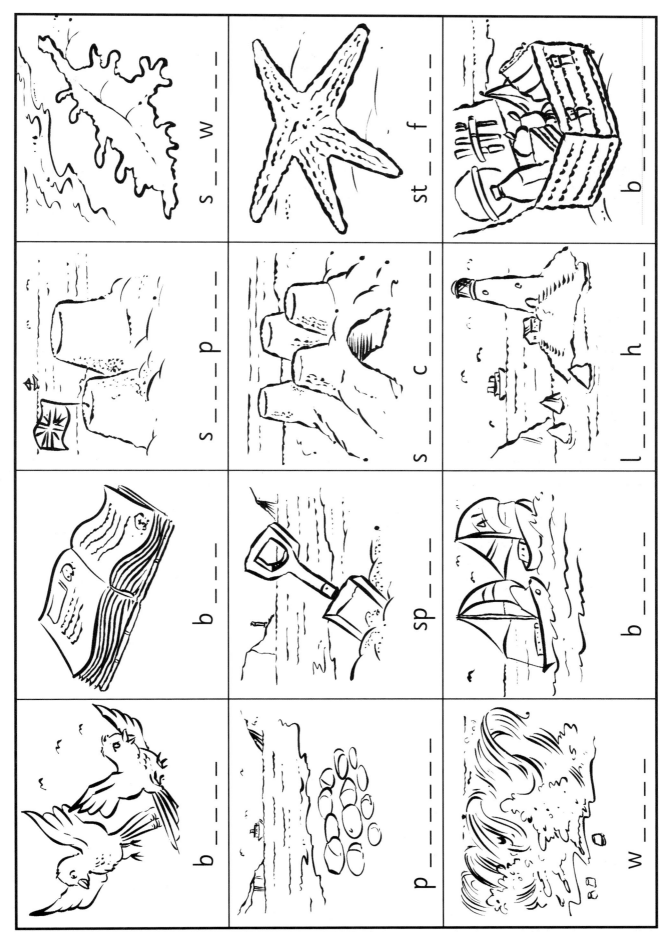

s __ w __

st __ f __

b __

s __ p __

s __ c __

l __ h __

b __

sp __

b __

b __

p __

w __

SECTION 7

FLASH CARDS FOR SOUND RECOGNITION AND WORD BUILDING

The flash cards in this section can be used to check children's knowledge of sounds. The letters are placed on the left of the cards so that the cards can be overlapped and the letter strings or words can be seen in their entirety.

You may find it helpful to make more than one copy of these sheets, preferably on card, and either laminated or covered with self-adhesive transparent film.

Activities include:

1. Say a word and ask the children with the same initial or final sound to hold up their card.
2. Hold up a card and ask children for words that begin with, end with, or have that sound in them.

3. Use the cards to blend words appropriate to the section that the children are working on. For example give out the cards to a group. Say a word and ask children who have the letters for that word to come out and put themselves in the correct order to make the word.
4. Give a pile of cards to a group of children and ask them to make as many words as they can using each card only once. At the end of the session ask the children to read out the words they have made, or to stand up holding the cards for the other children to guess the words.

a	b	c
d	e	f
g	h	i
j	k	l

m	n	o
p	q	r
s	t	u
v	w	x

sh	z	y
sc	th	ch
sp	sn	sk
ll	ff	st

ss	zz	ck
ea	ee	oa
ie	oe	ai
ay	oi	oy

ow	ou	oo
ir	er	ar
ear	ur	or
ore	oar	eer

SECTION 8

WORD LISTS FOR SOUND BOOKS

Start a new sound book for this section using a standard-sized book. To include all seventy lists in one book you will need to divide the page across the middle so that two lists will fit on a page, one below the other. Use books ruled with 11 mm feint so that children can add words they have found. Using lines prevents these added words from running into one another. The lists adhere closely to the order in which the sounds are introduced, starting from Section 3, and to the Phonic Check Sheet in Section 10.

To help children to recognise the patterning of words, and to be able to use the 'sounds like' or 'looks like' principles, words on a list with similar letter strings follow each other. Alternatively, one word may develop from the previous one e.g. end – bend – mend – send; span – spank; crisp – crispy; hair – hairy – fairy – fairly. This helps them to see that an unknown word may only mean the adding or changing of a single letter of a known word, and not that a complete new word has to be learnt. By bringing in this kind of redundancy to learning, children gain confidence in approaching new words for both reading and writing.

After the children have worked the copymaster using a particular blend, digraph or diphthong, give the child the appropriate list and go through it with them before it is pasted in their sound books and taken home. When a child is confident that a sound is known they can draw a smiley face ☺ at the bottom of the page in their sound book.

Go through the books with the children regularly to see that the words are being learnt, and to verify the progress that is being made. Give visual rewards in return, such as smiley faces, stickers or stars, or by ticking the smiley face the child has drawn. This system provides encouragement to both parents and children to continue the good work.

List 1	List 3	List 5	List 7	List 9
shall	chaff	thick	than	flag
shelf	chap	thin	that	flan
shell	chat	think	them	flap
shift	chatty	thank	then	flash
ship	check	thing	this	flip
shock	chick	thong	thus	flop
shop	chip	thud	with	glad
shot	chops	thump	their	glass
shrub	chum	thrill	there	glint
shunt	chuck	thrush	they	glum

List 2	List 4	List 6	List 8	List 10
dash	branch	bath	black	plan
rash	clinch	tenth	bled	plod
slash	flinch	pith	blob	plop
trash	pinch	fifth	blot	plot
fresh	winch	sixth	blush	plum
fish	bunch	ninth	clap	plus
wish	hunch	depth	clip	plug
Josh	lunch	moth	clop	split
brush	munch	cloth	cloth	splint
finish	French	froth	club	splash

List 11	List 13	List 15	List 17	List 19
slab	crab	fret	pram	stand
slam	crag	fresh	prim	stem
slap	cram	frill	prod	step
slim	crack	frisk	prop	still
slip	crash	frizz	profit	stick
slit	crept	frog	press	stink
slob	crib	from	prick	stop
slot	crisp	frock	print	stock
slug	crop	frost	prism	stun
slum	cross	Frank	prank	stuff

List 12	List 14	List 16	List 18	List 20
brat	drag	grab	trap	nest
bran	dram	gram	track	pest
brand	drum	Gran	tramp	vest
brim	drip	grid	trip	fist
brick	drop	grin	trill	mist
brisk	dress	grip	trick	twist
brash	drift	grill	trot	lost
brush	drill	grub	truck	just
branch	drink	gruff	trust	must
bring	drank	grunt	trunk	crust

List 21	List 23	List 25	List 27	List 29
span	sketch	scab	smack	swop
spank	skid	scalp	smash	swig
spell	skill	scamp	smell	swim
speck	skin	scan	smelt	swing
spend	skip	scant	Smith	swam
spit	skit	scum	smithy	swell
spill	skim	scuff	smog	swept
spin	skimp	scoff	smock	twig
spun	skimpy	Scot	smug	twin
spot	skunk	Ascot	smut	twist

List 22	List 24	List 26	List 28	List 30
clasp	task	scrub	snag	back
gasp	mask	scrap	snap	pack
grasp	flask	scratch	snack	sack
wasp	desk	script	snatch	neck
crisp	duck	sprat	snip	kick
crispy	husk	sprint	snick	lick
lisp	tuck	spring	sniff	lock
wisp	risk	strap	snob	rock
wispy	brisk	strip	snub	luck
aspect	frisky	strum	snug	yuck

List 31	List 33	List 35	List 37	List 39
cliff	bless	help	camp	and
quiff	cress	yelp	lamp	hand
skiff	dress	gulp	ramp	sand
sniff	press	pulp	limp	end
stiff	bliss	felt	bump	bend
scoff	cross	melt	dump	mend
bluff	floss	spelt	hump	send
gruff	gloss	kilt	jump	wind
scuff	buzz	quilt	lump	pond
scruffy	jazz	bolt	pump	fund

List 32	List 34	List 36	List 38	List 40
doll	craft	elk	ant	batch
shell	kept	silk	pant	catch
smell	left	milk	bent	hatch
spell	gift	milky	tent	fetch
swell	lift	bulk	went	ditch
drill	soft	hulk	sent	witch
frill	tuft	sulk	spent	stitch
skill	crept	elm	hint	notch
spill	slept	helm	mint	hutch
still	swept	film	font	clutch

List 41	List 43	List 45	List 47	List 49
bang	apple	need	food	made
gang	raffle	seed	cool	spade
long	paddle	seen	pool	lake
song	kettle	peel	room	snake
king	scribble	deep	moon	came
wing	candle	keep	soon	name
ring	angle	weep	hoop	ape
bring	jingle	sheep	boot	ate
string	thimble	feet	root	date
thing	twinkle	meet	zoo	cave

List 42	List 44	List 46	List 48	List 50
edge	bead	good	road	wide
hedge	each	hood	foal	like
ledge	peach	wood	goal	bike
judge	leak	foot	boat	bite
bridge	mean	cook	coat	kite
dodge	meat	look	goat	five
lodge	treat	took	float	mine
lodger	cream	book	throat	shine
badge	dream	brook	roast	smile
badger	stream	shook	toast	prize

List 51	List 53	List 55	List 57	List 59
code	nail	loud	cow	new
hole	snail	cloud	how	dew
home	pain	aloud	now	few
bone	train	noun	owl	flew
cone	paint	out	fowl	blew
note	day	scout	growl	chew
slope	may	shout	down	stew
those	way	about	brown	crew
froze	play	mouth	crown	screw
globe	stay	south	clown	threw

List 52	List 54	List 56	List 58	List 60
cube	oil	low	jaw	jar
duke	boil	glow	paw	car
mule	coil	crow	saw	card
rule	soil	grow	draw	hard
plume	coin	show	straw	bark
dune	join	snow	fawn	dark
June	moist	slow	lawn	park
use	boy	flow	hawk	arm
cute	joy	flown	crawl	farm
flute	toy	throw	shawl	start

List 61	List 63	List 65	List 67	List 69
her	or	could	deer	air
herb	cord	would	peer	fair
kerb	fork	should	cheer	lair
verb	form	bound	sheer	pair
jerk	born	found	sneer	chair
germ	torn	round	oar	stair
term	fort	ground	roar	hair
fern	sport	count	soar	hairy
stern	torch	mount	board	fairy
perch	north	fountain	hoard	fairly

List 62	List 64	List 66	List 68	List 70
fir	fur	ear	care	high
bird	curl	dear	dare	sigh
third	surf	fear	hare	thigh
girl	turf	gear	mare	fight
swirl	hurt	hear	glare	light
dirt	burn	near	scare	might
shirt	turn	rear	share	night
skirt	churn	year	snare	right
first	church	clear	spare	fright
thirst	burst	spear	stare	slight

GAMES, ACTIVITIES AND MASTER SHEETS

This section consists of a number of games, and some master sheets, which you can adapt for your class's needs or for those of a particular child. The games will last longer if they are copied, or glued, on to card and then covered with self-adhesive transparent film.

Copymaster 95: Bingo

This bingo type game is for up to six players, the words at the bottom are for the caller and need to be cut up. You may need to photocopy two sets of the caller's cards. Most words are on at least two cards so it encourages children to be sharp. When children get their bingo cards, give them a chance to go through the card and become familiar with the words it contains.

1. The caller's cards are shuffled and laid face down. The caller picks up a card and says the word without the players seeing it. The first to put up a hand or call 'mine' takes the card and places it face down over the matching card on their board.
2. An alternative way to play the game is for each player to take a bingo board, individual cards are placed face down in the middle of the table. Children take it in turns to pick up a card. They say the word and, if it is correct, place it face down on their bingo card, if it is not the card is returned, face down, to its original position.

Pelmanism

Make another copy of the bingo sheet on card and cut up all the words and trim off any lines. Lay the cards face down.

The first player selects one card, says the word and then does the same with a second card. If they are the same the player keeps the 'trick', if not the cards are returned to their original place. The winner of a 'trick' has another turn. By remembering the position of returned cards children can help themselves win more 'tricks'.

Copymasters 96 and 97: 'Alphabet sun' and 'Alphabet spiral'

This activity can be used in conjunction with Sections 2, 4 and 6.

Section 2   Children work through the alphabet in turn finding one or more words which begin with each letter and writing them in the space provided.
Section 4   A word has to be found that begins with each

letter in turn and includes an initial, or final, blend or digraph.
Section 6   A word has to be found for each letter which includes a double vowel, or vowel digraph, or a group of letter strings which you have selected.

Variations include:

1. The number of words they can list in a given time.
2. The number of words they find for each letter or a given letter.
3. The length of time it takes to find at least two words for each letter.
4. The total number of words found.
5. The first child to list fifty words.

Copymasters 98 and 99: Trawling for fish

This game is for two players. Cut Copymaster 98 on the dotted line and cut up the cards on Copymaster 99. Provide the players with counters.

The individual cards are placed in a pile, face down, on the table. Children take it in turns to turn over a card and say the word. If the word is in their net, they keep the card and cover the fish with a counter. If the word is not in their net the card is put at the bottom of the pile.

Copymasters 100 and 101: Stegosaurus

Four sets of 'bony plates' are supplied for the stegosaurus. Set 1 makes words with short vowel sounds, Set 2 words which begin with consonant digraphs and blends, Set 3 words which end with digraphs and blends and Set 4 words with double vowels; a difficult one because the words to be made are split at the double vowel. Each group makes a complete sequence irrespective of which 'plate' is laid first because they are all part of one chain, as shown on the copymaster.

There are lots of words children can make from each set of plates, this is part of the task, we want children to play around with the 'plates' making real and nonsense words and deciding which is which. The harder task is to keep making and remaking words until a sequence of complete words is found which allows all the plates to be laid. This is a good task for pairs and small groups.

Copymasters 102 and 103: Sound wheels

Cut the copymaster on the lines, cut out the circle and fix it to the baseboard with a brass fastener through the centre.

Variations include:

1. The number of words they list in a given time.
2. Taking one letter or letter string on the wheel, list the number of words they make by matching it with the letters on the base board or vice versa.
3. Find at least two words for each letter or ending, how long did it take?
4. Total the number of words found.
5. The first child to find twenty words.

Two versions of the game are supplied, and a couple of masters so you can make other sound wheels suited to the growing competence of your pupils.

Copymasters 104 and 105

These copymasters are suitable for a range of games and activities. The sheets are not identical. The second sheet gives extra copies of the vowels essential in word building.

Snap
Copy and cut up both lists to form cards.

Deal out the cards and play the usual way, but say the sound in common instead of 'snap'.

Find the Sound
Copy and cut up both lists to form cards.

1. Each child in a group has up to five cards. Say 'bat – b' and ask children to hold up a card with the letter for the given sound if they have one.
2. Say a word and ask children to show you a card with its initial sound.
3. Say a sound, ask the children to show the card (or cards) for that sound and give a word that begins with (or includes) the sound.
4. Hold up a card and ask children to hold up any card (or cards) they may have which would go with it to make a word. Those with suitable cards hold their card(s) next to yours and say the word.

Pelmanism
Copy and cut up the first list to form cards. Play as for Copymaster 95.

Pick a Sound
Copy and cut up one list to form cards.

Place the cards face down. Children take it in turns to turn over a card then say its sound and a word that begins or ends with that sound. If correct they keep the card.

Clock words
This game is played in a similar way to clock patience but using letters instead and forming words. The cards are placed face up to represent the numerals on a clock. If the cards are placed in the positions for 12, 3, 6, and 9 first and then in the other numeral positions it is easier for the children to set out. The remaining cards are placed face down in a stack in the centre.

Each child takes it in turn to make as long a word as possible with the cards, setting out the word in front of themselves. The child says the word made out loud for the others to check its correctness. He or she then fills in the vacant spaces on the clock with other letters from the stack before the game passes to the next player. The game continues until all the letters are used, or no further words can be made. Points are awarded to each child for the words made according to the number of letters.

Copymaster 106: Spinners
Print or mount the spinners on card. Sharpen a 5 cm piece of thin doweling and put it through the centre. Working alone, the child spins the spinner and puts other letters with the letter string to make a word. A list is made of the words formed.

Working in groups of up to four children they take it in turns to twist the spinner and say a word which includes that letter string. If they cannot make a word the spinner is passed to the next child. The children either make their own lists of the words they make, or a single one is made with the words listed in a column.

Copymaster 107: Ladders
Cut each copymaster so you have six ladders.

1. Write a sound at the top of the ladder. Children collect words either beginning with that sound or with that sound in them and write them on a rung of the ladder. How quickly can they complete the ladder?
2. Write a word at the bottom of the ladder and the children move up the ladder changing a letter each time, adding a letter or taking one away, to form a new word.
3. Children write a word on the lowest rung and use the last letter (or letter string) of that word to begin a word on the next rung. How long does it take to complete the ladder?

Copymaster 108: Fly game
This game is for two players. Copy the sheet, cut up the words and place face down. (Some words are not real words.) Provide the players with counters. The first player turns over a card, says the word, places a counter on the first space on their half of the fly and keeps the card. If the child cannot say the word or turns over a non-word it is returned to its position and laid face down. The first child to reach the fly's eyes is the winner.

117

bun	cat	hut	bat	cut	fan
dog	net	pot	hot	log	pit
tin	hot	get	sun	let	cat
but	cog	fun	can	fit	hen
mat	lot	pen	let	pin	fan
win	get	sat	sit	bat	ten
win	cog	fun	but	pin	can
net	lot	pen	ten	fit	sun
bun	hut	sat	sit	mat	pot

bun	sat	let	hot	pit	cut
mat	can	get	cog	pin	but
win	ten	net	log	tin	sun
dog	hen	lot	sit	bat	fun
fan	pen	pot	fit	hut	cat

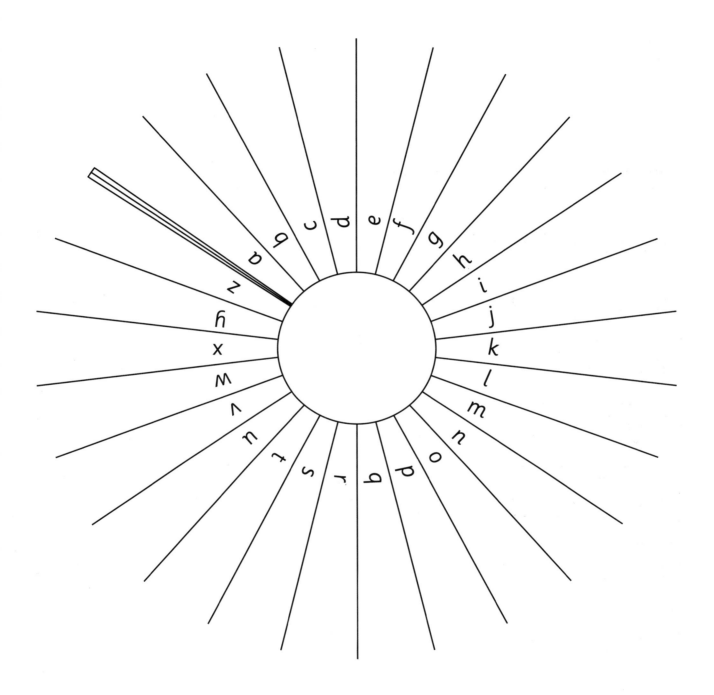

Alphabet Sun – Copymaster 96

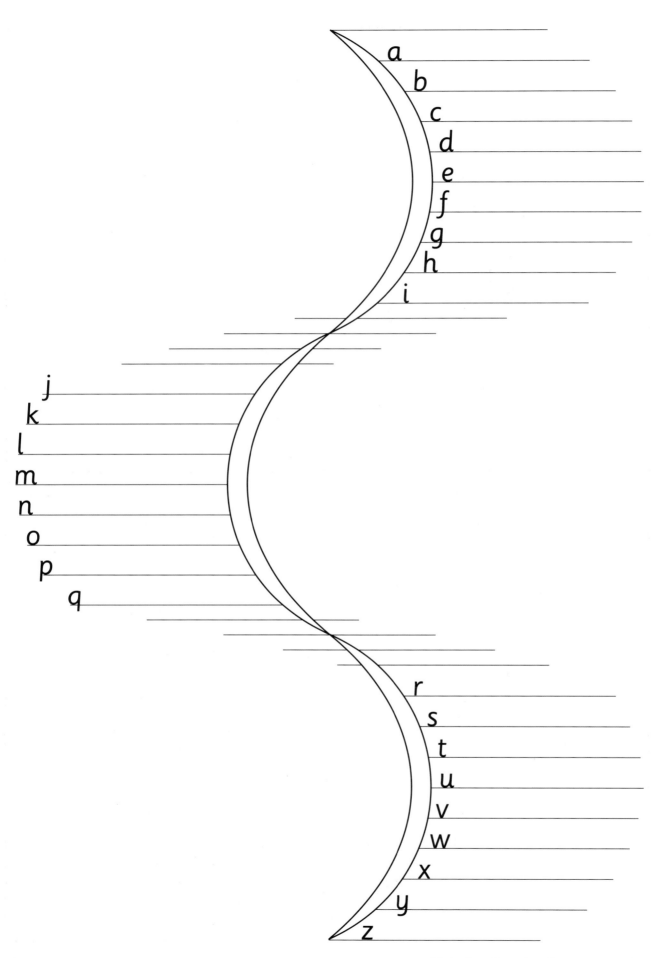

a
b
c
d
e
f
g
h
i

j
k
l
m
n
o
p
q

r
s
t
u
v
w
x
y
z

Alphabet Spiral – Copymaster 97

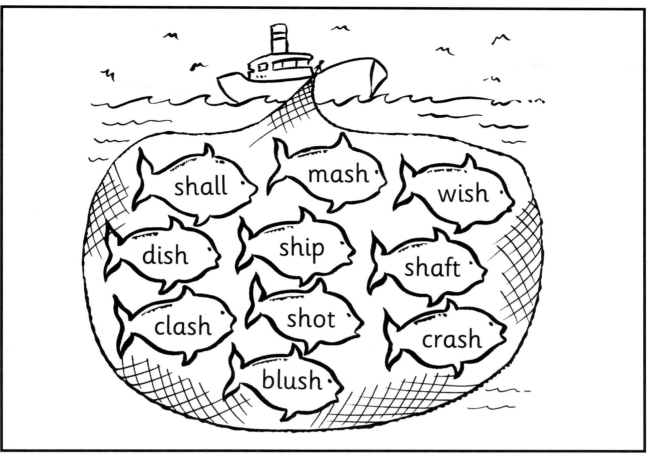

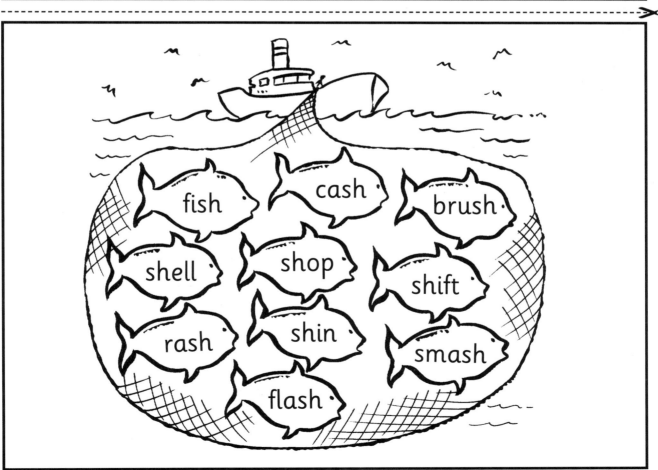

shin	cash	shell	rash	fish
smash	shift	brush	flash	shop
ship	dish	wish	mash	shall
blush	shot	crash	shaft	clash

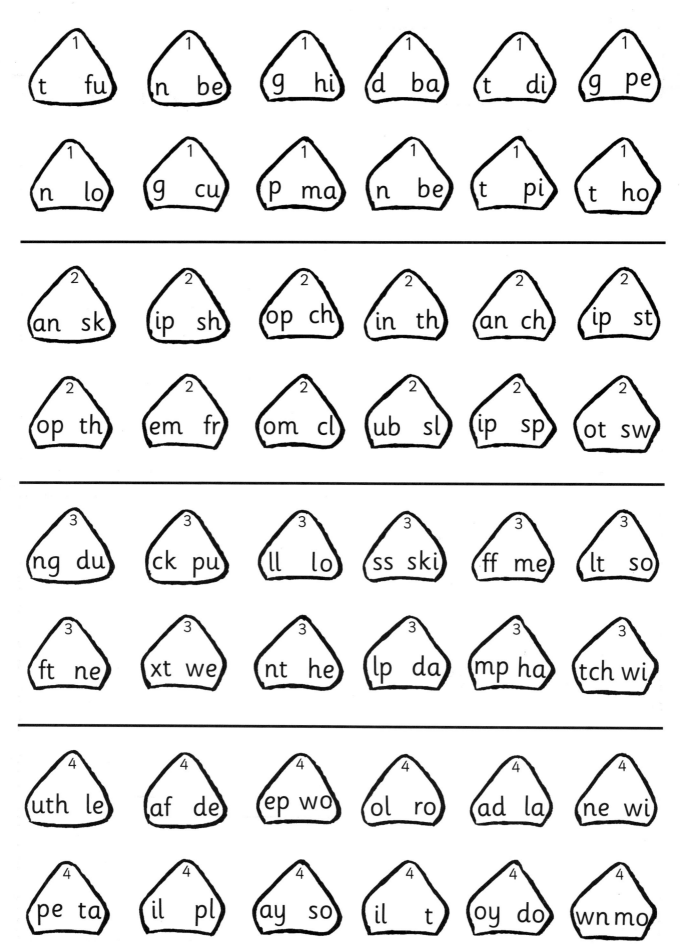

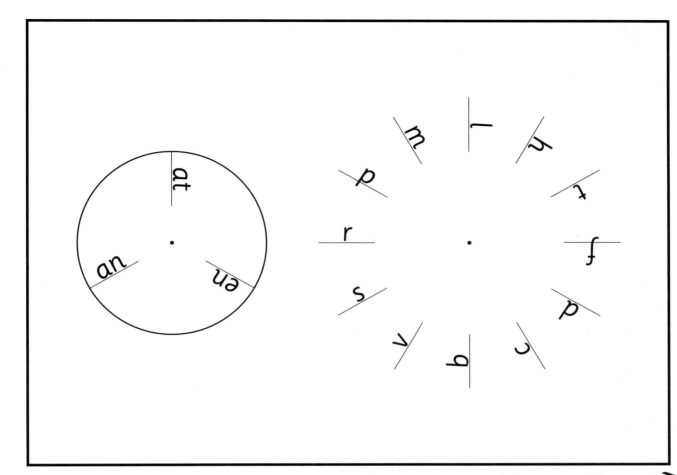

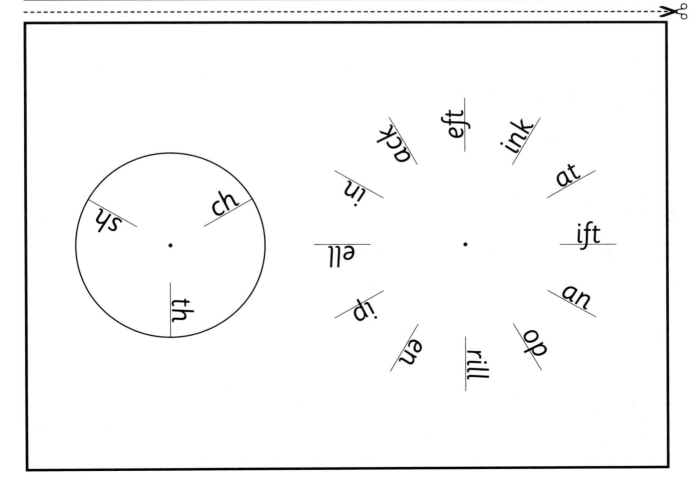

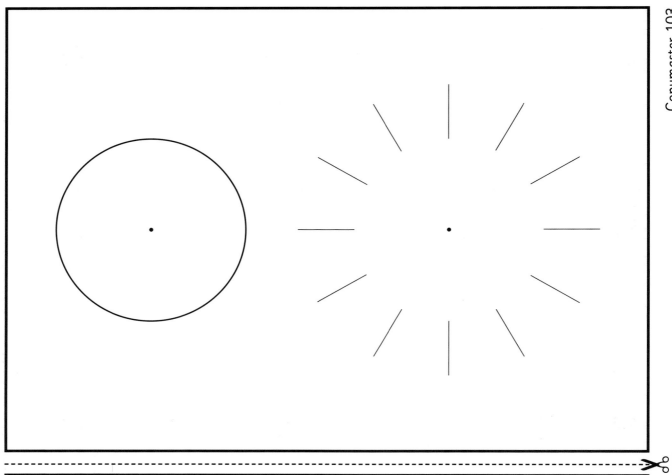

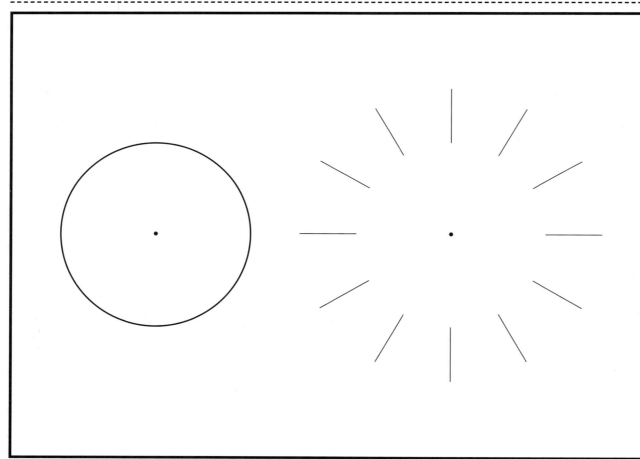

a	b	c	d	e	f	g
h	i	j	k	l	m	n
o	p	q	r	s	t	u
v	w	x	y	z	th	ch
sh	ff	ll	ss	zz	ck	ng

a	a	e	e	i	i	o
o	u	u	b	c	d	f
g	h	j	k	l	m	n
p	q	r	s	t	v	w
y	th	sh	ch	ff	ll	ss

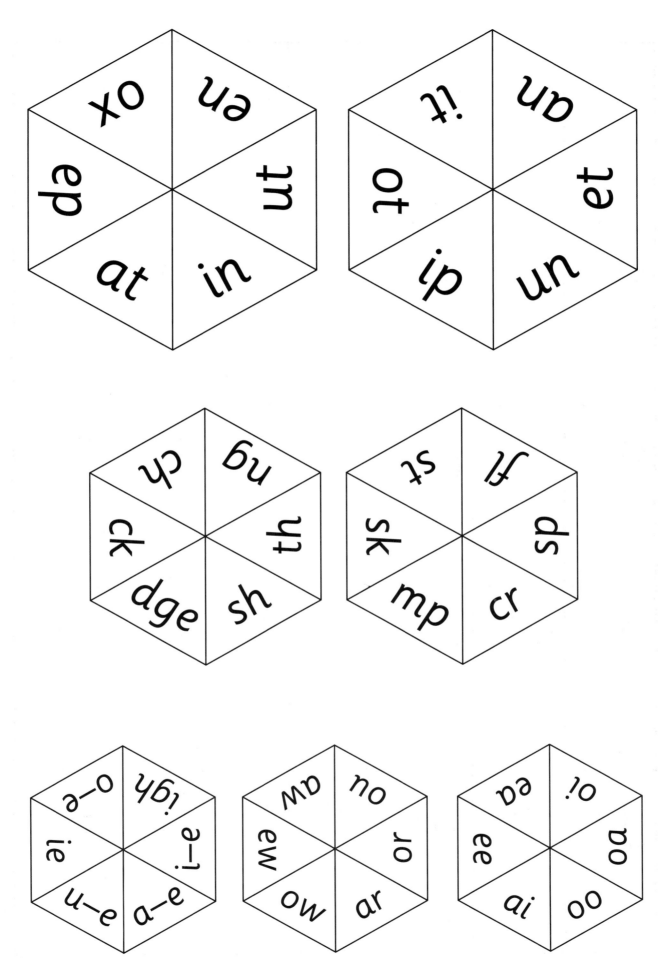

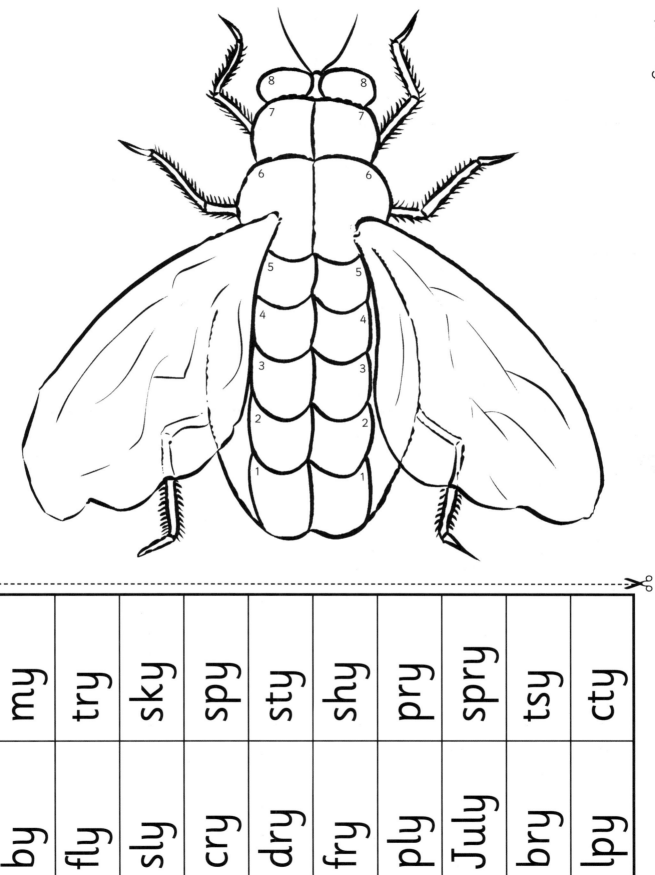

my	by
try	fly
sky	sly
spy	cry
sty	dry
shy	fry
pry	ply
spry	July
tsy	bry
cty	lpy

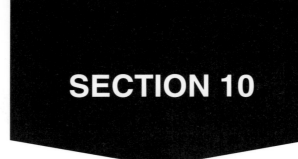

SECTION 10

Copymaster 109: Colour Chart

A number of the early copymasters ask children to colour sounds a specific colour. Colour in the block to the left of the word on the chart. If you want the words in alphabetical order cut the list in half lengthways and mount it on card. If you cover the chart with self-adhesive transparent film before putting it up for little fingers to walk over it will last a long time.

Copymaster 110 and 111: Letters to Parents

'Using the Sound Books' and *'Playing the Games'*

Give these letters out at a meeting with parents, for them to keep for reference, or send them home with the first book or game to explain to the parents what to do and why.

Space has been left at the top to place a heading strip from school note paper, or for you to type it in.

You may wish to cut off the appropriate rule for a game and send it home in a box or wallet with the cards, rather than all the rules at once. They do sometimes get lost!

Copymaster 112: Phonic Check Sheet

All the sounds in *The Phonics Book* are included in this list.

If you use a different coloured pen every time you do a check it will:

- confirm the stage a child has reached
- indicate a child's speed of progress
- highlight any sticking points or weaker areas.

Copymaster 113: Word list for the Phonic Check Sheet

This word list is set out in the same order as the Phonic Check Sheet. You may find it helpful to use these words rather than ask for the sound alone. The children say the word first, then you point to the sound and ask them to say it. Put a piece of card under the line of words to isolate it and to stop the child taking fright at such a long list.

Colour Chart

	blue		orange
	black		pink
	brown		purple
	green		red
	grey		yellow

Dear Parent,

Using the Sound Books

The English language is made up of two kinds of words, those we can build by knowing the sounds like '*cat*' or '*scamp*' and those we have to learn as wholes, 'look and say' words like '*was*' or '*here*'. Our pupils will learn both how to build words and ways of learning 'look and say' words.

The children are to bring home their Sound Books to show you with the lists of words we have been working on. Each letter or letter string learnt will add new lists to the book so it will become both a working book and a record of your child's progress.

Please go through the words with your child, read them through together and encourage your child to read them to you. Words are built by using the sounds of the letter and blending them together slowly. Run your finger under a word sounding and blending the whole word as you say it: '*caaat*' (not '*cuh-a-tuh*'), '*haaannnd*' (not '*huh-a-nn-duh*'), so making the sounds flow through the word not splitting the word into single sounds.

Be patient, work at your own child's pace, especially in the beginning. Encourage your child to be confident, to have a go, as their knowledge of sounds and blending grows.

By spending five minutes a day with these lists you will be helping your child to learn the letter sounds, how to build words and to read at an earlier age. Your child will gain the confidence to work out new or unfamiliar words.

An additional bonus will be that through encouraging your child to talk with you, and by sharing in the work they do in school, you and your child will build a closer relationship.

Yours sincerely,

Dear Parents,

Playing the Games

Playing games with children is worthwhile. It helps them to learn how to co-operate, to wait their turn, and to develop a sense of right and wrong, as well as enjoying time with you. Below are the rules for some of the games your child will be bringing home. Please see that the games come back to school each day so that others can use them too.

Bingo
Give the players time to go through the words on the card before you begin to play.
1. The cards are shuffled and laid face down. The caller picks up a card and says the word without the players seeing it. The first to put up a hand or call 'mine' takes the card and places it face down over the matching card on their board.
2. The cards are placed face down in the middle of the table. The first player picks up a card, says the word and, if it is correct, places it face down on their bingo card, if not the card is returned, face down, to its original position. Now it is the next player's turn.

Pelmanism
Lay the cards face down. The first player selects one card, says the word then selects a second one. If they are the same the player keeps the 'trick', if not the cards are returned to their original places. The winner of a 'trick' has another turn. Remember the position of returned cards so you can use them when a matching card turns up. This game can be played with other packs of cards provided there are two copies of each card.

Pick a sound
Place the cards face down. Take it in turns to turn over a card, say its sound and a word that begins or ends with that sound. If the player is correct they keep the card.

Snap
Deal out cards and play the usual way but say the sound or word instead of 'snap'.

Clock words
A patience game, or for up to four players. Make a clock face with the cards by placing cards, face up, at 12 and 6, the 3 and 9. Next put two between each quarter. The remaining cards are put in a pile. The first player makes as long a word as possible with the cards, sets out the word, says it, then fills in the spaces on the clock with other letters from the pile. The games passes from one to the other until all the letters are used or the game has reached an impasse. Award points for each word according to the number of letters in the word, a three- lettered word gets 3 points. The winner is the one with the most points.

Spinners
Take it in turns to twist the spinner and say a word which includes that letter string. If a player cannot make a word the spinner is passed to the next child. Make lists of the words you make.

Fly
This game is for two players, who need eight counters each. Place the words face down. (Some are not real words.) The first player turns over a card, says the word, places a counter on the first space on their half of the fly and keeps the card. If the child cannot say the word or turns over a non-word it is returned to its position and laid face down.

We hope you enjoy playing these games with your child and joining in the progress they are making. All card and board games develop children's logic and speed up their thinking so do go on to play many more games with your child and have fun together.

Thank you for your help,

Yours sincerely,

Phonic Check Sheet

Date ....

Pupil's name ....   School ....

Single sounds: a_____   e_____   i_____   o_____   u_____

                  d_____   l_____   n_____   r_____   s_____   t_____

                  b_____   f_____   m_____   p_____   v_____   w_____

                  c_____   g_____   h_____   k_____   y_____

                  j_____   q_____   x_____   z_____

Consonant blends and digraphs:

Initial blends   sh_____   ch_____   th (voiced)_____   th (unvoiced)_____

                  bl_____   cl_____   fl_____   gl_____   pl_____   sl_____   spl_____

                  br_____   cr_____   dr_____   fr_____   gr_____   pr_____   tr_____

                  st_____   sp_____   sk_____   sc_____   sm_____   sn_____

                  sw_____   tw_____

Final blends   -sk_____   -sp_____   -st_____

                  -ck_____   -dd_____   -ff_____   -ll_____   -ss_____   -zz_____

                  -ct_____   -ft_____   -lt_____   -nt_____   -pt_____   -xt_____

                  -lk_____   -lm_____   -lp_____   -mp_____ -nd_____   -nk_____

                  -tch_____   -ng_____   -dge_____   -ddle_____   -pple_____

                  -ttle_____   -ndle_____   -ngle_____   -nkle_____

Double vowels and diphthongs:

Double vowel   ea_____   ee_____   oa_____   (b)oo(k)_____   (m)oo(n)_____

Marker 'e'   a-e_____   i-e_____   o-e_____   u-e_____

Diphthongs   ai_____   ay_____   oi_____   oy_____   ou_____   oun_____

              (c)ow_____   (sn)ow_____   aw_____   ew_____

              ie_____   igh_____   ight_____ -y_____

Affective 'r':   ar_____   er_____   ir_____   or_____   ur_____

                  ear_____   eer_____   oar_____   are_____   air_____

Word List for Phonic Check Sheet

and	egg	it	on	up
dog	lip	net	ran	sun
ten	bin	fun	man	pet
van	wet	cut	gap	hen
kit	yes	jam	quit	box
zip	ship	chop	then	thin
blot	clip	flat	glad	plus
slot	splash	brim	crab	drum
frog	grab	pram	trim	stop
spin	skip	scan	smug	snap
swim	twig	brisk	lisp	lost
duck	add	off	ill	hiss
buzz	pact	left	felt	went
kept	next	sulk	film	help
hump	end	think	match	thing
wedge	riddle	apple	bottle	candle
tangle	twinkle	cream	creep	boat
book	moon	cake	bike	vote
tune	rain	day	join	toy
loud	found	cow	snow	straw
flew	pie	high	light	try
dark	kerb	girl	sport	burn
clear	deer	roar	stare	chair

BLUEPRINTS ENGLISH RESOURCES

The **Blueprints** series provides a very wide range of carefully structured resources for English in primary schools. Alongside the core Blueprints English books for Key Stages 1 and 2, the developing Blueprints Primary English series, of which *The Phonics Books* is part, provides more detailed coverage of essential key skills.

A further invaluable resource is the *Blueprints: Reading Activities Resource Bank*. This provides a comprehensive compendium of reading activities and games. It consists of 147 photocopiable pages of puzzles, jigsaws, dominoes and race games. Structured around the publication Individualised Reading and the sight vocabulary of most common reading schemes, it enables classroom teachers and assistants to make up a huge bank of reading games at a fraction of the commercial cost. We have reproduced two sample pages from the book for interest below.

Further information about this and other Stanley Thornes books can be obtained from the address and telephone number on the reverse of the title page.

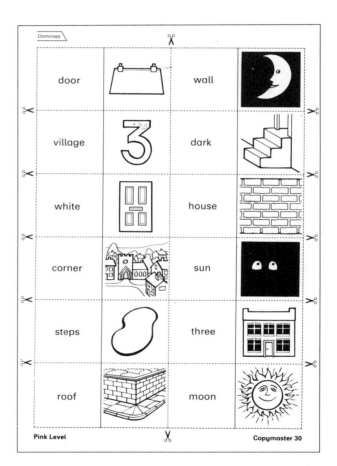

Reduced pages from Blueprints: Reading Activities Resource Bank